D0524454

Impact maths 2 R

1

2

3

4

5

6

7

8

9

heinemann.co.uk
✓ Free online support
✓ Useful weblinks
✓ 24 hour online ordering

01865 888058

Heinemann

Inspiring generations

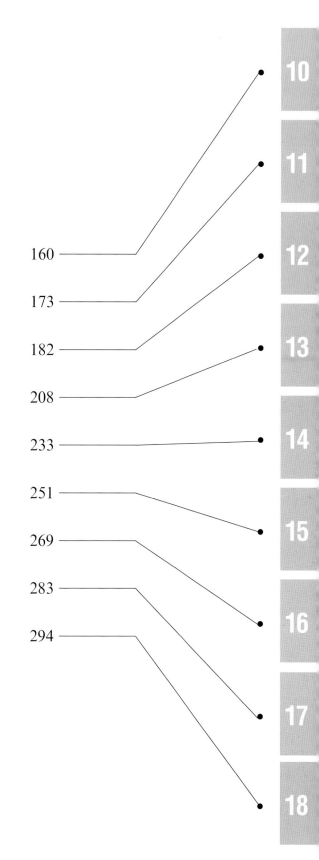

About this book

Impact maths provides a complete course to help you achieve your best in your Key Stage 3 Mathematics course. This book will help you understand and remember mathematical ideas, solve mathematical problems with and without the help of a calculator and develop your mental maths skills.

Exercises you should try without the help of a calculator are marked with this symbol:

Finding your way around

To help you find your way around when you are studying use the:

- **edge marks** shown on the front pages – these help you get to the right unit quickly

- **contents list** and **index** – these list all the key ideas covered in the book and help you turn straight to them.

- **links** in the margin – these show when an idea elsewhere in the book may be useful:

There is more about powers on page 5.

Remembering key ideas

We have provided clear explanations of the key ideas you need throughout the book with **worked examples** showing you how to answer questions. **Key points** you need to remember look like this:

■   **The distance around the edge of a shape is its perimeter.**

and are listed in a **summary** at the end of each unit.

Investigations and information technology

Two units focus on particular skills you need for your course:

- **using and applying mathematics** (unit 17) – shows you some ways of investigating mathematical problems.

- **calculators and computers** (unit 18) – shows you some ways of using calculators and computers and will help with mental maths practice.

Heinemann is an imprint of Pearson Education Limited, a company incorporated in England and Wales, having its registered office at Edinburgh Gate, Harlow, Essex, CM20 2JE.
Registered company number: 872828
Heinemann is a registered trademark of Pearson Education Limited

First published 2000

ISBN: 978 0 435017 96 5

10
13

Designed and typeset by Tech-Set Ltd, Gateshead, Tyne and Wear
Illustrated by Barry Atkinson, Barking Dog and Tech-Set
Cover design by Miller, Craig and Cocking
Printed and bound in China (CTPS/13)

Acknowledgements

The authors and publishers would like to thank the following for permission to use photographs:
p59: Hague Historical Museum. p115: Corbis/Joel W. Rogers. p130: NASA. p134: Corbis/Galen Rowell. p134: Corbis/Wild Country. p233: NASA/Roger. p237: Corbis/Gunter Marx. p258: Corbis/Nik Wheeler. p271: Corbis/Reuters New Media Inc. p272: Photofusion

Cover Photo by Tony Stone Images.

Publishing team

Editorial
Philip Ellaway
Shaheen Hassan
Nigel Green
Harry Smith
Sarah Caton
Katherine Pate
Anne Russell

Design
Phil Richards
Colette Jacquelin
Mags Robertson
Peter Morris

Production
David Lawrence
Jason Wyatt

Author team
David Benjamin
Sue Bright
Tony Clough
Gareth Cole
Diana DeBrida
Brian Fillis
Ray Fraser
Peter Jolly

David Kent
Gina Marquess
Christine Medlow
Graham Newman
Sheila Nolan
Keith Pledger
Ian Roper
Mike Smith
John Sylvester

Tel: 01865 888058   www.heinemann.co.uk

Contents

4 Probability

5 Decimals

6 Percentages

7 Shape and measure

8 Positive and negative numbers

13 Handling data

14 Formulae and equations

15 Perimeter, area and volume

1 Number

1.1 Using large numbers

You can write any whole number in the decimal number system using just these digits:

    0, 1, 2, 3, 4, 5, 6, 7, 8, and 9

■ **The value of a digit depends on its place in the number.**

To read large numbers you can write them in a place value table:

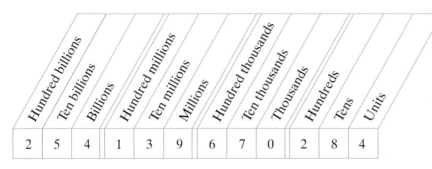

Notice that the place value of each number is ten times bigger than the place value of the number on the right of it.

You say "two hundred and fifty four billion, one hundred and thirty nine million, six hundred and seventy thousand, two hundred and eighty four".

Example 1

What is the value of the 4 in each number?

(a) 245   (b) 1054   (c) 4290   (d) 5400

(a) 4 tens   (b) 4 units
(c) 4 thousands   (d) 4 hundreds

Example 2

For each number say:
(i) how many billions there are
(ii) how many millions there are
(iii) how many thousands there are

(a) 35 487 204 328   **(b)** 534 839 500 928

(a) **(i)**   35 billions   **(b)** **(i)**   534 billions
    (ii)   35 487 millions   **(ii)**   534 839 millions
    (iii) 35 487 204 thousands   **(iii)** 534 839 500 thousands

Example 3

Put these numbers in order of size:

507 296 403 205   48 329 047 643
    48 677 987   269 293
875 293 582 849   898 701 732
                    754 894

You could order them first into numbers starting with ...

billions: 507 296 403 205
                    48 329 047 643
                    875 293 582 849

millions: 48 677 987
                    898 701 732

thousands: 269 293
                    754 894

Next order the billions, millions and thousands ...

billions: 875 293 582 849
                    507 296 403 205
                    48 329 047 643

millions: 898 701 732
                    48 677 987

thousands: 754 894
                    269 293

Exercise 1A

1 For each number say:
    (i)   how many billions there are.
    (ii) how many millions there are.
    (iii) how many thousands there are.
    (a) 347 409 273 560   **(b)** 63 208 355 845
    (c) 408 048 222 593   **(d)** 7 098 358 023

2 Put these numbers in order of size, starting with the largest:

(a)

35 898
872 409 371 978
48 992 273
487 377 760 375
231 337
3 587 337 909
500 000 000

(b)

93 821 580
289 035 387 431
77 837
89 034 711 839
276 997
457 870 909
298 045 756 998

(c)

8 521 580
189 035 387 431
488 992 273
587 377 760 375
231 337
452 970 909
248 998

1.2 Multiples, factors and primes

This section will help you find out more about the properties of multiples, factors and primes.

$1 \times 5 = 5$
$2 \times 5 = 10$
$3 \times 5 = 15$
$4 \times 5 = 20$
$\vdots$
$33 \times 5 = 165$
$34 \times 5 = 170$
$\vdots$

- **The multiples of 5 are the answers in the 5 times multiplication table.**

  Any whole number multiplied by 5 is a multiple of 5:

  5, 10, 15, 20, 25, 30, ... 165, 170, ... etc.

- **The factors of a number are those whole numbers that divide into it exactly.**

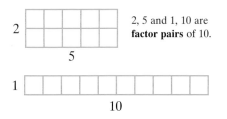

2, 5 and 1, 10 are **factor pairs** of 10.

These rectangles are made with 10 squares. The lengths of the sides are the factors of 10: 1, 2, 5 and 10.

$1 \times 1 = 1$ $1 \times 2 = 2$ $1 \times 5 = 5$ $1 \times 10 = 10$
$2 \times 1 = 2$ $2 \times 2 = 4$ $2 \times 5 = 10$
$3 \times 1 = 3$ $3 \times 2 = 6$
$4 \times 1 = 4$ $4 \times 2 = 8$
$5 \times 1 = 5$ $5 \times 2 = 10$
$6 \times 1 = 6$
$7 \times 1 = 7$
$8 \times 1 = 8$
$9 \times 1 = 9$
$10 \times 1 = 10$

10 only appears in the 1, 2, 5 and 10 multiplication table.

- **Numbers that have exactly two factors are prime numbers. These factors are the number itself and 1.**

  2, 3, 5, 7, 11, 13, 17, 19, 23, ...   **are prime numbers,**
  1, 4, 6, 8, 9, 10, 12, 14, 15, 16, ...   **are not prime numbers.**

Exercise 1B

1 True or false. Explain your answers:

(a) There is always a multiple of 4 between any two multiples of 5.

(b) There is always a multiple of 5 between any two multiples of 4.

(c) If you add a multiple of 4 to a multiple of 6 you always get a multiple of 2.

(d) If you add a multiple of 3 to a multiple of 5 you always get an odd number.

2 Complete these statements:

(a) There is always a multiple of ..... between any two multiples of 7.

(b) If you add a multiple of 6 to a multiple of 9 you always get a multiple of .....

3 (a) Copy this table and complete it using all the numbers from 1 to 16.

	Even	Odd	Not a multiple of 4	multiple of 4
Less than 10				
Multiple of 3		9		
Not a multiple of 3				
Greater than 10				

9 is odd and a multiple of 3.

(b) Make up your own puzzle similar to this one.

4 Which of these numbers can be divided by 2, 3 and 5?
24, 30, 55, 60, 150, 16, 81, 720, 210

5 Find all the factors of:

(a) 45   (b) 39   (c) 100

6 What are the three factor pairs of 20?

7 Which of these numbers are prime numbers?
2, 4, 7, 9, 15, 17, 21, 23, 41, 42, 95, 101, 153

1.3 Powers of numbers

If you want to multiply the same number by itself you can write it as a power.

■ **4^5 is '4 to the power of 5'**
  $4^5 = 4 \times 4 \times 4 \times 4 \times 4 = 1024.$

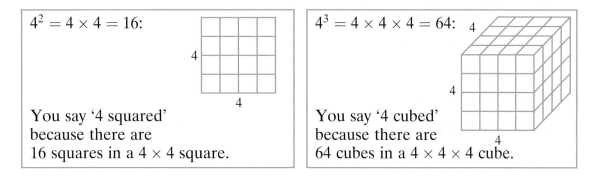

$4^2 = 4 \times 4 = 16$:

You say '4 squared' because there are 16 squares in a 4×4 square.

$4^3 = 4 \times 4 \times 4 = 64$:

You say '4 cubed' because there are 64 cubes in a $4 \times 4 \times 4$ cube.

The opposite of a power is called a **root**.

■ **4 is the square root of 16 because $4 \times 4 = 16$**
  4 is the cube root of 64 because $4 \times 4 \times 4 = 64$
  4 is the fifth root of 1024 because $4 \times 4 \times 4 \times 4 \times 4 = 1024$

Example 4

Write $7 \times 7 \times 7 \times 7 \times 7 \times 7$ as a power of 7

$7 \times 7 \times 7 \times 7 \times 7 \times 7 = 7^6$

Example 5

Write 625 as a power of 5

$625 = 5 \times 5 \times 5 \times 5 = 5^4$

Example 6

Write 100 000 000 as a power of 10

There are eight zeros after the 1 so $100\,000\,000 = 10^8$

Example 7

Work out 9^3

$9^3 = 9 \times 9 \times 9 = 729$

Exercise 1C

1 Write as powers:

   (a) $8 \times 8 \times 8 \times 8 \times 8$ **(b)** $7 \times 7 \times 7 \times 7$

   (c) $3 \times 3 \times 3 \times 3 \times 3 \times 3$ **(d)** $10 \times 10 \times 10$

2 Work out:

(a) 5 squared   (b) 2 cubed

(c) 2^4 (d) 5 cubed

(e) 3^4 (f) 10^7

(g) 8^3 (h) 0^6

(i) 9^3 (j) 1^7

(k) 3 to the power of 5   (l) 5 to the power of 4

3 Work out:

(a) 100 squared   (b) 10 cubed

(c) 0 cubed   (d) the square root of 81

(e) the cube root of 27   (f) the fourth root of 16

(g) the cube root of 1   (h) the fourth root of 625

(i) the fifth root of 32   (j) the seventh root of 10 000 000

4 Write:

(a) 8 as a power of 2   (b) 36 as a power of 6

(c) 27 as a power of 3   (d) 100 000 as a power of 10

(e) 64 as a power of 4   (f) 128 as a power of 2

(g) 81 as a power of 3   (h) 125 as a power of 5

(i) 9×9 as a power of 3   (j) $25 \times 25 \times 25$ as a power of 5

(k) $4 \times 4 \times 4$ as a power of 2   (l) $16 \times 16 \times 16$ as a power of 4

Hint: In part (i) think of 9 as 3×3

5 You can write 12 as the difference of two square numbers.
You can write 13 as the sum of two square numbers.
Which numbers up to 20 can be written as either the difference or the sum of two square numbers?

$12 = 16 - 4$
$13 = 9 + 4$

6 Which prime numbers less than 100 can be written as the sum of two square numbers?

| 73 | $=$ | 9 | $+$ | 64 |
| prime number | | square number | | square number |

7 Which prime number less than 100 can be written as the sum of two cube numbers?

8 Activity You need cubes for this activity.

(a) How many cubes do you need to build each of the double sided staircases shown?

(b) Investigate how many cubes you need to build other double sided staircases.
Try to explain anything you discover.

(c) What is the tallest double sided staircase you can build using

(i) 50 cubes (ii) 200 cubes
(iii) 500 cubes (iv) 1000 cubes

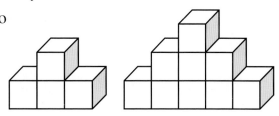

9 Investigate the relationship between these two patterns of numbers:

1
$1 + 2$
$1 + 2 + 3$
$1 + 2 + 3 + 4$

1^3
$1^3 + 2^3$
$1^3 + 2^3 + 3^3$
$1^3 + 2^3 + 3^3 + 4^3$

1.4 Rounding to the nearest 10, 100, 1000 ...

You can use rounding to make bigger numbers easier to use.
You can round to the nearest ...

... ten

... thousand

... depending on the size of the number.

■ **To round to the nearest 10:**
Look at the digit in the units column
If it is less than 5 round down
If it is 5 or greater round up

■ **To round to the nearest 100:**
Look at the digit in the tens column
If it is less than 5 round down
If it is 5 or greater round up

... and so on for rounding to the nearest 1000, 10 000, ...

Example 8

Write 47 103 524 to the nearest:

(a) million   (b) ten million   (c) thousand

(a) 47 000 000   (b) 50 000 000   (c) 47 104 000
    or 47 million   or 50 million

Example 9

There are 138 000 butterfly species in the world, to the nearest 1000.
How many species could there actually be?

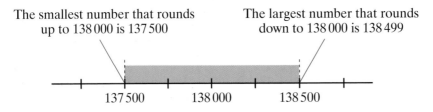

The smallest number that rounds up to 138 000 is 137 500

The largest number that rounds down to 138 000 is 138 499

So there are between 137 500 and 138 499 butterfly species in the world.

Exercise 1D

1 Write each of these numbers correct to the nearest 10

(a) 47   (b) 83   (c) 75   (d) 78

(e) 243   (f) 737   (g) 895   (h) 4386

'Correct to the nearest 10' is the same as rounding to the nearest 10.

2 Round each of these numbers to the nearest 100

(a) 487   (b) 943   (c) 654   (d) 84

(e) 2843   (f) 7357   (g) 7983   (h) 4386

3 Write each of these numbers correct to the nearest thousand

(a) 5837   (b) 6724   (c) 4275

(d) 34 531   (e) 45 123   (f) 731

(g) 728 275   (h) 311 840   (i) 89 833

(j) 799 542   (k) 7 374 489   (l) 99 364 834

4 Write each of these numbers correct to the nearest million

(a) 25 843 765   (b) 7 503 624   (c) 16 287 455   (d) 834 659 051

(e) 864 523   (f) 12 391 267   (g) 2 678 748 604   (h) 111 653 789 640

(i) 19 561 833   (j) 99 832 842

5 Round each number in the table as shown

	Number	Round to the nearest ...		Number	Round to the nearest ...
a	48	Ten	g	8643	Thousand
b	764	Hundred	h	573 095	Hundred Thousand
c	420	Hundred	i	468 430	Ten Thousand
d	63 584	Thousand	j	79 650	Thousand
e	85 323	Ten Thousand	k	4653	Hundred
f	784 750	Hundred Thousand	l	43 296	Ten Thousand

1.5 Significant figures

You will not always be asked to round a number to the nearest 10, 1000, ...
You sometimes have to round to a number of **significant figures**.

■ **The first significant figure in a number is the first non-zero digit on the left. The second significant figure is the next digit to the right.**

Example 10

What is the first significant figure of

(a) 386   (b) 25 673

(a) The first significant figure is 3
(b) The first significant figure is 2

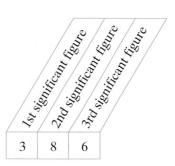

■ **To round to 1 significant figure:**
Look at the second significant figure,
If it is less than 5 round down
If it is 5 or greater round up

Example 11

Round to 1 significant figure:

(a) 378   (b) 23 137   (c) 10

(a) The second significant figure is 7 so round up:
$$378 = 400 \text{ to 1 s.f.}$$

(b) The second significant figure is 3 so round down:
$$23\,137 = 20\,000 \text{ to 1 s.f.}$$

(c) The second significant figure is 0 so round down:
10 to 1 s.f. is still 10.

> You can write 1 significant figure as 1 s.f.

Example 12

Round each number to 1 significant figure to get an approximate answer to:

(a) 4378×276 (b) $78\,413 \div 352$

(a) 4000×300
$= 12\,000 \times 100$
$= 1\,200\,000$

> Remember: to multiply by 300, multiply by 3 then multiply by 100

(b) $80\,000 \div 400$
$= 800 \div 4$
$= 200$

> To divide by 400, divide by 100 then divide by 4

Exercise 1E

1 Round each number to 1 significant figure to get an approximate answer to:

  (a) 537×8265 (b) $36\,423 \times 6498$

  (c) $7623 \div 432$ (d) $19\,462 \div 4723$

  (e) $56\,342 \div 2507$ (f) $562 \times 7273 \times 3538$

  (g) $23\,285 \times 45\,723 \times 762$ (h) $465\,987\,035 \times 73\,098$

  (i) $5843 \div 11\,598$

2 For each calculation, round to 1 s.f. to find the correct answer from the cloud.

  (a) $14\,287 \times 2746$ (b) 7813×257

  (c) $17\,589 \div 5863$ (d) $32\,752 \div 178$

  (e) $79\,422 \times 854$ (f) $633\,620 \div 2437$

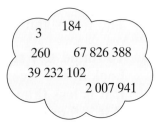

3   184
260   67 826 388
39 232 102
2 007 941

3 Copy the table but round each number to 1 significant figure. True or false?

Country	Population
China	1 215 293 000
USA	262 693 000
Mexico	89 872 000
UK	58 541 000
Kenya	29 520 000
Iraq	20 645 000
Laos	4 791 000
Mauritius	1 141 000

  (a) The population of the USA is about ten times the population of Kenya.
  (b) For every person in Laos there are 12 people in the UK.
  (c) There are 100 Chinese people for every Mauritian.

Make up a statement like this of your own.

1.6 Checking answers by estimation

It is easy to make a mistake by pressing the wrong key on your calculator.

■ **You can check that a calculator answer is in the right region by rounding each number to estimate the answer.**

Example 13

Find an approximate answer to $7183 + 819 + 4820$.

Round each number to one significant figure then add.

```
7183 rounds to   7000
 819 rounds to    800
4820 rounds to   5000
                12 800
```

So $7183 + 819 + 4820$ is about 12 800.

Exercise 1F

1 Round each number to the nearest 100, then add or subtract to find an approximate answer to:

  (a) $887 - 324$ **(b)** $931 - 296$
  (c) $552 + 387$ **(d)** $899 + 502$
  (e) $398 - 285$ **(f)** $721 - 240$
  (g) $486 + 209$ **(h)** $807 - 521$
  (i) $827 - 394 + 674$ **(j)** $137 + 851 + 827$
  (k) $714 - 387 - 132$ **(l)** $471 + 203 - 586$

2 Round each number to the nearest 1000, then add or subtract to find an approximate answer to:

(a) $6812 + 2466$ (b) $4358 + 2988$

(c) $8838 - 4091$ (d) $6570 - 1853$

(e) $8947 + 7682$ (f) $7862 + 813$

(g) $7419 - 4827$ (h) $26\,709 - 18\,564$

(i) $4293 - 1642 + 3734$ (j) $8817 - 3084 - 2523$

(k) $2154 + 5398 - 4805$ (l) $4384 + 2462 + 2652$

3 Find an approximate answer for each sum then choose a number from the cloud which could be the correct answer.

(a) $487 + 246 + 175$ (b) $813 - 469 + 257$ (c) $829 + 752 - 483$

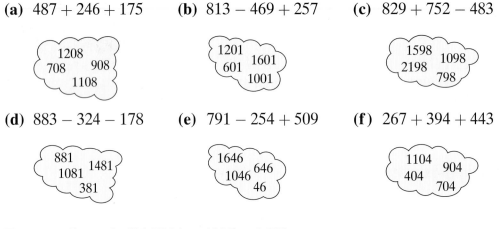

         1208   1201   1598

708   908   601   1601   2198   1098

        1108   1001   798

(d) $883 - 324 - 178$ (e) $791 - 254 + 509$ (f) $267 + 394 + 443$

       881   1646   1104

1081   1481   1046   646   404   904

     381   46   704

4 Four pupils each did $7291 + 4825 + 3428$ on their calculators.
Who got the correct answer?
Use rounding to get an approximate answer first.

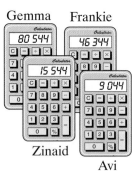

Gemma   Frankie

Zinaid

Avi

5 Who got the correct answer to this calculation:

$8724 - 3291 + 6597$

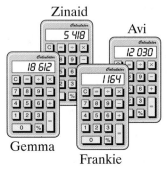

Zinaid

Avi

Gemma

Frankie

1.7 Using inverse operations to check calculator answers

Sometimes rounding won't help you decide if an answer is right.

Tim adds $89\,260 + 12\,789 - 7983$ on his calculator and gets the answer 92 266.

He estimates the answer as:

$$90\,000 + 10\,000 - 8000 = 92\,000$$

which is about right.

If you check this with your calculator you will see that the answer is actually 94 066.

Tim entered $89\,260 + 12\,789 - \mathbf{9}783$ so he got the wrong answer.

Think of a calculation as a number machine:

Use the inverse number machine ...

... you should get your original number back.

If you do then your answer is probably correct.

■   **To check a calculation is correct you can use the inverse number machine. This is called using inverse operations.**

Example 14

Ray works out 5892×4723 on his calculator.
He gets the answer 27 880 944.
Check his answer using inverse operations.

$27\,880\,944 \div 4723 = 5903.2276$

so his answer is wrong.

Example 15

Michèle works out $38\,953\,026 \div 7266$ on her calculator.
She gets the answer 5361.
Check her answer using inverse operations.

$5361 \times 7266 = 38\,953\,026$

so her answer is correct.

Exercise 1G

1 Use inverse operations to check which calculations are correct:

(a) $36\,924 + 8765 - 12\,329 = 33\,360$
(b) $48\,293 + 17\,547 + 3849 = 69\,599$
(c) $128\,963 - 12\,894 + 5839 = 121\,908$
(d) $84\,397 - 7629 - 6581 = 71\,087$
(e) $794\,386 - 48\,629 - 15\,092 = 730\,465$
(f) $18\,369 + 25\,286 + 5439 = 48\,694$

2 Use inverse operations to check which calculations are correct:

(a) $8896 \div 64 = 139$ (b) $8925 \times 257 = 2\,131\,815$
(c) $28\,401\,067 \div 7429 = 3823$ (d) $26\,530\,254 \div 6219 = 4254$
(e) $5231 \times 764 = 3\,982\,732$ (f) $754 \times 9635 = 65\,074\,790$

3 Use inverse operations to find the missing numbers:

(a) $\ldots\ldots + 763 = 2311$ (b) $\ldots\ldots - 1284 = 3643$
(c) $\ldots\ldots \times 497 = 4\,436\,222$ (d) $\ldots\ldots \div 678 = 154$
(e) $\ldots\ldots + 8531 + 4675 = 19\,169$
(f) $\ldots\ldots - 9137 - 8134 = 62\,581$

Summary of key points

1 The value of a digit depends on its place in the number.

2 The multiples of 5 are the answers in the 5 times multiplication table.
   Any whole number multiplied by 5 is a multiple of 5:
   5, 10, 15, 20, 25, 30, ... 165, 170, ... etc.

3 The factors of a number are those whole numbers that divide into it exactly.

   For example, 1, 2, 5 and 10 are the factors of 10.

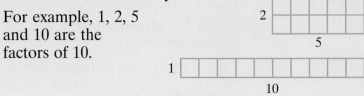

4   Numbers that have exactly two factors are prime numbers. These factors are the number itself and 1. 2, 3, 5, 7, 11, 13, 17, 19, 23, ... are prime numbers, 1, 4, 6, 8, 9, 10, 12, 14, 15, 16, ... are not prime numbers.

5   4^5 is '4 to the power of 5'
$4^5 = 4 \times 4 \times 4 \times 4 \times 4 = 1024$.

6   4 is the square root of 16 because $4 \times 4 = 16$
4 is the cube root of 64 because $4 \times 4 \times 4 = 64$
4 is the fifth root of 1024 because
$4 \times 4 \times 4 \times 4 \times 4 = 1024$

7   To round to the nearest 10:
Look at the digit in the units column
If it is less than 5 round down
If it is 5 or greater round up

8   To round to the nearest 100:
Look at the digit in the tens column
If it is less than 5 round down
If it is 5 or greater round up

9   The first significant figure in a number is the first non-zero digit on the left. The second significant figure is the next digit to the right.

10   To round to 1 significant figure:
Look at the second significant figure,
If it is less than 5 round down
If it is 5 or greater round up

11   You can check that a calculator answer is in the right region by rounding each number to estimate the answer.

12   To check a calculation is correct you can use the inverse number machine. This is called using inverse operations.

2 Angles

2.1 Measuring angles

- **Any angle less than 90° is called an acute angle.**
- **Any angle more than 90° but less than 180° is called an obtuse angle.**
- **Any angle more than 180° is called a reflex angle.**

Example 1

State the angle type of each of these angles:

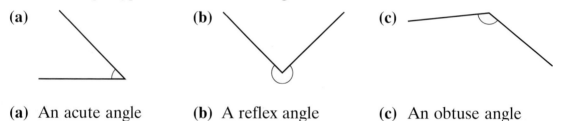

(a) **(b)** **(c)**

(a) An acute angle   **(b)** A reflex angle   **(c)** An obtuse angle

Exercise 2A

For each angle:

(a) write down the angle type

(b) make an accurate measurement of the angle.

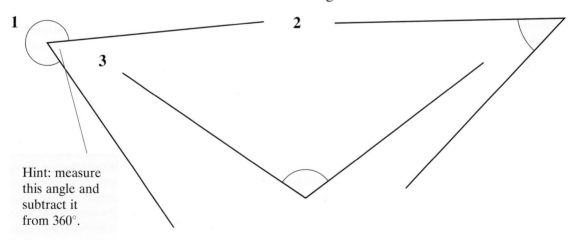

Hint: measure this angle and subtract it from 360°.

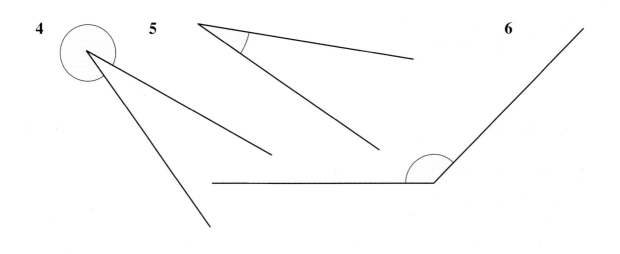

2.2 Drawing angles

Example 2

Draw an angle of 160°.

1 Start with a straight line.

2 Place the centre of your protractor
   at the end of the line.

3 Count around the scale of the
   protractor from 0° to 160°.

4 Draw a second line through 160° to make the angle.

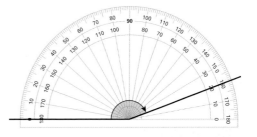

Example 3

Draw an angle of 315°.

Use the same method as before for measuring reflex angles.
You need to draw the angle of $360° - 315° = 45°$.

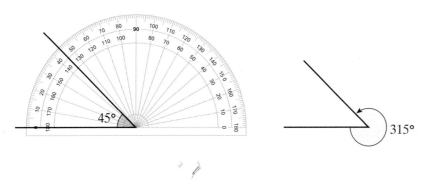

Exercise 2B

For each angle:

(a) write down the angle type

(b) make an accurate drawing of the angle.

1 120°	**2** 65°	**3** 200°	**4** 30°
5 325°	**6** 45°	**7** 135°	**8** 317°
9 55°	**10** 100°	**11** 15°	**12** 236°
13 86°	**14** 133°	**15** 250°	**16** 125°
17 265°	**18** 194°	**19** 167°	**20** 63°

2.3 Estimating angles

Example 4

Estimate the size of angle x.

This acute angle is slightly smaller than half a right angle (45°).
A good estimate would be 40°.

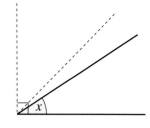

Example 5

Estimate the size of angle y.

First estimate the size of acute angle t.
Angle t is just less than $\frac{2}{3}$ of a right angle (60°).
A good estimate would be 50°.
An estimate for obtuse
angle y is $180° − 50° = 130°$.

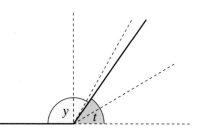

Exercise 2C

For each angle write down:

(a) the angle type

(b) an estimate for the size of the angle.

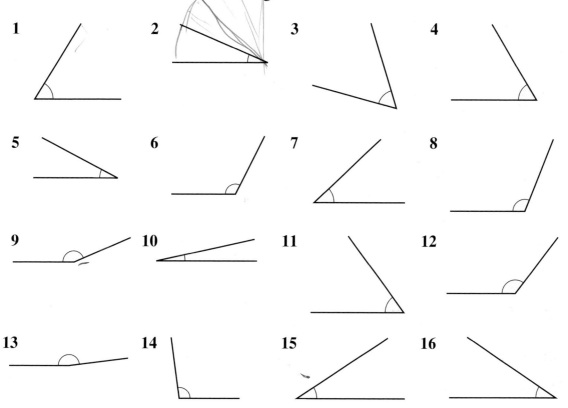

1   2   3   4

5   6   7   8

9   10   11   12

13   14   15   16

2.4 Angles on lines and at points

■ **Any two angles that are drawn on a straight line will always add up to 180°:**

$a + b = 180°$

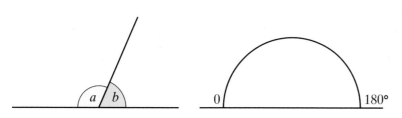

■ **In a full circle there are 360°.**

$$a + b + c = 360°$$

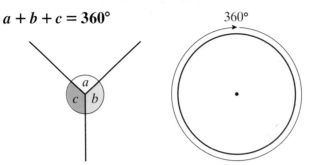

■ **When two lines cross they form two pairs of angles opposite each other that are the same size:**

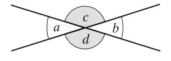

$$a = b, \quad c = d$$

Example 6

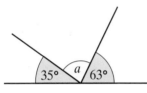

Find angle a.

$a = 180° - 35° - 63°$
$\quad = 82°$

Example 7

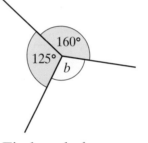

Find angle b.

$b = 360° - 160° - 125°$
$\quad = 75°$

Example 8

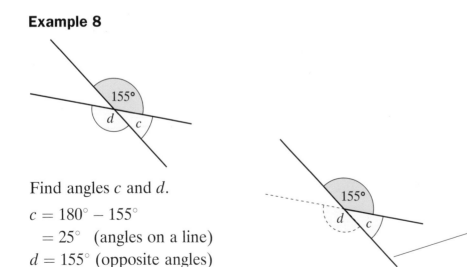

Find angles c and d.

$c = 180° - 155°$
$\quad = 25°$ (angles on a line)
$d = 155°$ (opposite angles)

Angles drawn on a straight line add up to $180°$

Exercise 2D

In each question find the value of the letter or letters.

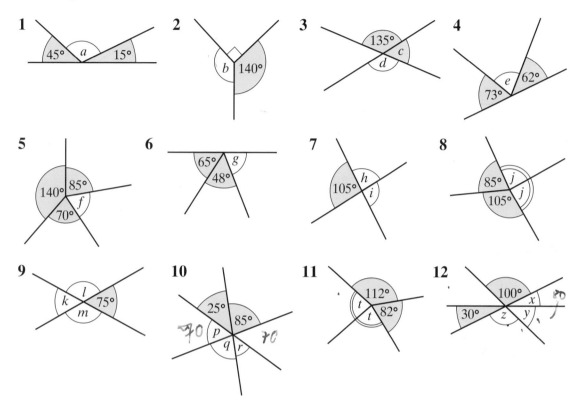

1 45° a 15°

2 b 140°

3 135° c d

4 e 62° 73°

5 140° 85° f 70°

6 65° g 48°

7 105° h i

8 85° j j 105°

9 k l 75° m

10 25° 85° ꟻ0 p q r 70

11 112° t t 82°

12 100° x 30° z y

2.5 Angles in shapes

Angles are shown in diagrams in two ways.

(a)

100° x 82° z y

(b)

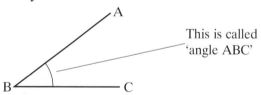

A

This is called 'angle ABC'

B ———— C

By using a letter for each angle

By using the points that make the angle

Example 9

Use the points to describe angle *x* in the diagram.

x = angle ABC

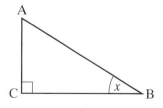

A

C x B

Example 10

Which lower case letter is angle PSQ?

angle PSQ = angle f

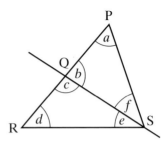

Exercise 2E

1 Use points to describe the angle shaded in each diagram.

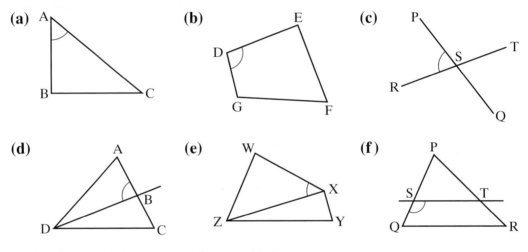

(a)

(b)

(c)

(d)

(e)

(f)

2 Write down the lower case letter which represents these angles:

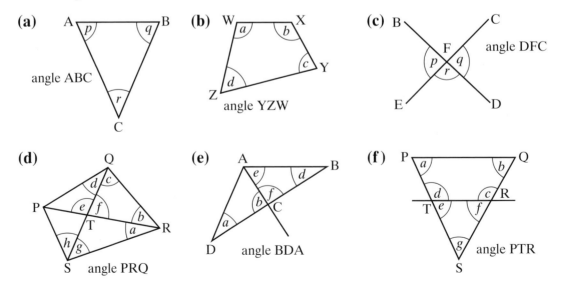

(a) angle ABC

(b) angle YZW

(c) angle DFC

(d) angle PRQ

(e) angle BDA

(f) angle PTR

2.6 Angles in triangles and quadrilaterals

1 Draw any triangle on a piece of paper.

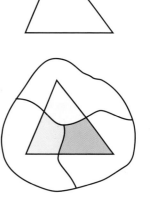

2 Tear the triangle into three pieces so you have three angles.

3 Put the pieces together again so that the points of the angles are together.

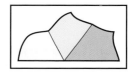

The three angles together make a half turn or semicircle.
The three angles together add up to 180°.
This will work for any triangle.

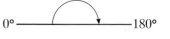

■ **The three angles of any triangle add up to 180°.**

Now try doing the same for any quadrilateral.

You should find that the angles add up to 360°.

■ **The four angles of any quadrilateral add up to 360°.**

Example 11

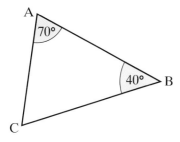

Find angle ACB.

All three angles add up to 180°.
ACB = 180° − 70° − 40°
     = 70°

Example 12

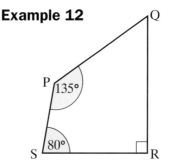

Find angle PQR.

All four angles add up to 360°.
PQR = 360° − 135° − 80° − 90°
     = 55°

Exercise 2F

Find the missing angle in each shape:

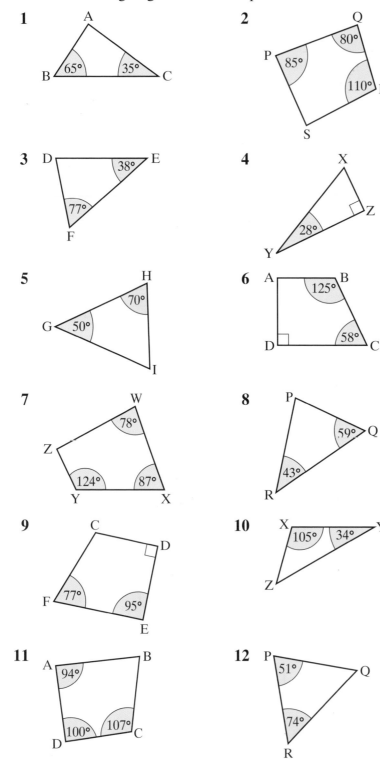

1

A

B 65° 35° C

2

Q

P 85° 80°

110° R

S

3 D 38° E

77°

F

4

X

Z

28°

Y

5

H

70°

G 50°

I

6 A B

125°

D 58° C

7

W

78°

Z

124° 87°

Y X

8 P

59° Q

43°

R

9 C

D

F 77°

95°

E

10 X 105° 34° Y

Z

11

A 94° B

100° 107°

D C

12 P 51°

Q

74°

R

2.7 Calculating with angles

■ **The angles of an equilateral triangle are 60° each.**

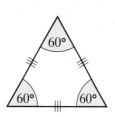

In an isosceles triangle two of the sides are the same length. This means that the angles next to each of these equal sides will be equal in size: $a = b$.

■ **Two of the angles in an isosceles triangle are equal in size.**

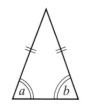

These properties can help you calculate angles in triangles.

Example 13

Find angle b.

The two angles at the base of the isosceles triangle are equal.

There are 180° in a triangle.

$$b = 180° - 50° - 50°$$

So $b = 80°$

You can combine your knowledge of angles on lines and points with your knowledge of angle properties in triangles.

Example 14

Find angle a.

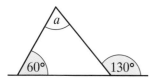

First find the size of the other angle inside the triangle:

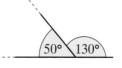

since $50° + 130° = 180°$
(angles on a straight line)

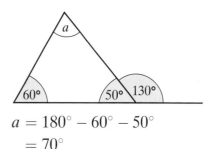

$$a = 180° - 60° - 50°$$
$$= 70°$$

Exercise 2G

In each question find the value of the letter or letters.

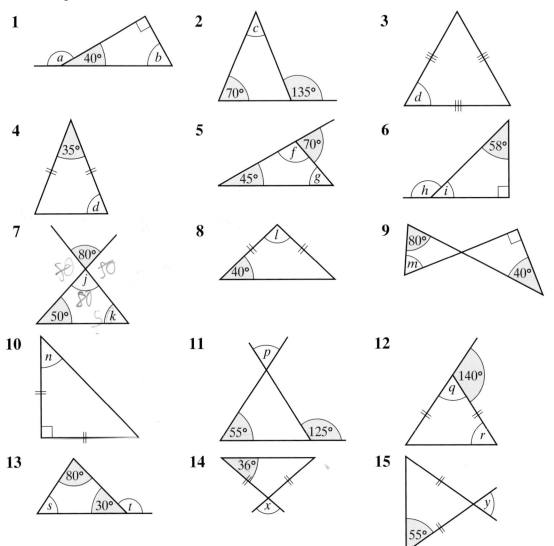

2.8 Angles in polygons

The angles inside a polygon are called interior angles.
Exterior angles can be drawn by extending an edge of the polygon.

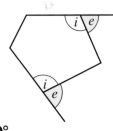

Angles on a straight line add up to 180°:

So $i + e = 180°$

■ **In a polygon the interior angle + the exterior angle = 180°.**

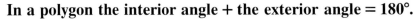

This pentagon has 5 sides, 5 interior angles and 5 exterior angles.

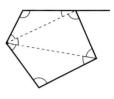

All these angles could be different sizes, but the *total* of the angles can be found.

From a vertex of the pentagon draw lines to divide the shape into triangles.

All interior angles are made up from the angles in the triangles.

In each triangle the total of the angles is 180°.

Total size of the interior angles $= 3 \times 180° = 540°$.

■ **The total sum of the interior angles of a polygon can be found by dividing the polygon into triangles.**

Exercise 2H

1 Copy and complete the table.

Polygon	Number of sides	Sum of interior angles	
Triangle	3	180°	
Quadrilateral	4	360°	
Pentagon	5	540	108
Hexagon	6	720	120
Heptagon	7	900	128,5
Octagon	8	1080	135
Nonagon	9	1260	140
Decagon	10	1440	144
Dodecagon	12	1620	135

2 Find a rule connecting the number of sides, *n*, of a polygon, and the total sum of its interior angles.

3 Calculate the sum of the interior angles of polygons with the following numbers of sides:

   (a) 15   **(b)** 20   **(c)** 40   **(d)** 50

4 Calculate the number of sides of polygons with the following sums of their interior angles:

   (a) 2160°   **(b)** 1620°   **(c)** 4140°   **(d)** 4500°

2.9 Regular polygons

A regular polygon has sides that are all the same length, and therefore angles that are all the same size.

The sum of the interior angles of a hexagon is 720°.

Since all the interior angles are the same size in a regular hexagon, each interior angle is $720 \div 6 = 120°$.

The exterior angles of a regular hexagon are all $180° - 120° = 60°$.

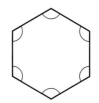

Example 15

Find the size of the interior angles of a regular polygon with 5 sides.

The sum of the interior angles is 540°.

$$540° \div 5 = 108°$$

The interior angles are 108°.

Exercise 2I

1 Copy and complete the table.

Regular polygon	Number of sides	Size of interior angle	Size of exterior angle
Triangle	3	60	
Square	4	90	
Pentagon	5	108	
Hexagon	6	120°	60°
Heptagon	7		
Octagon	8		
Nonagon	9		
Decagon	10		
Dodecagon	12		

2 Find rules connecting the number of sides, n, of a regular polygon, with

    (a) the size of its interior angle

    (b) the size of its exterior angle.

3 Find the number of sides of a regular polygon with an exterior angle of size:

(a) 40°   (b) 24°   (c) 20°   (d) 15°

4 Find the number of sides of a regular polygon with an internal angle of size:

(a) 144°   (b) 140°

5 Find the size of each unknown angle:

(a)

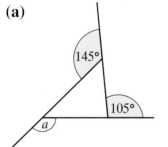

(b)

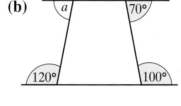

(c)

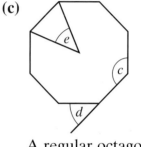

A regular octagon

2.10 Angles between parallel lines

■ **Straight lines are parallel if they are the same distance apart at every point.**

■ **Parallel lines are shown by arrowed lines.**

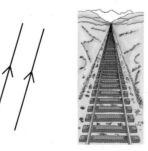

Draw two parallel lines and an intersecting line which crosses them.

The two angles *a* and *b* are always equal:

$a = b$

The two angles are called **alternate** angles, or **Z** angles, when they are in this position.

The two angles *c* and *d* are always equal:

$c = d$

The two angles are called **corresponding angles**, or **F** angles, when they are in this position.

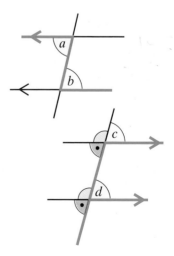

The two angles e and f add up to give $180°$:

$e + f = 180°$

The two angles e and f are called **supplementary** angles, or **C** angles, when they are in this position.

■   **Alternate or Z angles are always equal:**

$a = b$

■   **Corresponding or F angles are always equal:**

$c = d$

■   **Supplementary or C angles add up to 180°:**

$e + f = 180°$

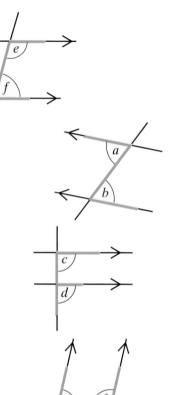

Example 16

Find the value of each letter in the diagram.

$a = 120°$ (alternate angles)
$b = 120°$ (corresponding angles)
$c + 120° = 180°$ (supplementary angles)
$c = 60°$

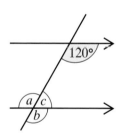

Exercise 2J

In each question find the value of the letter or letters.

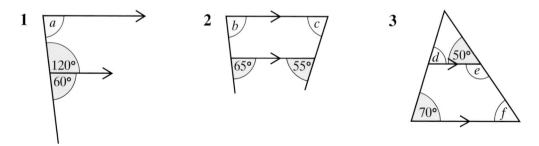

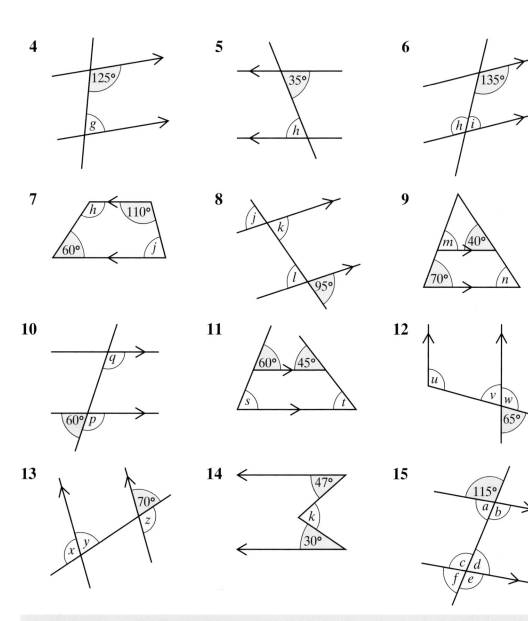

4

5

6

7

8

9

10

11

12

13

14

15

Summary of key points

1 Any angle less than 90° is called an acute angle.

2 Any angle more than 90° but less than 180° is called an obtuse angle.

3 Any angle more than 180° is called a reflex angle.

4 Any two angles that are drawn on a straight line will always add up to 180°:

$$a + b = 180°$$

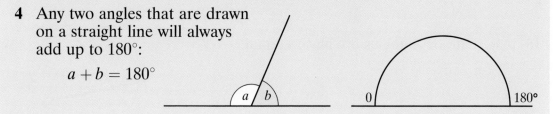

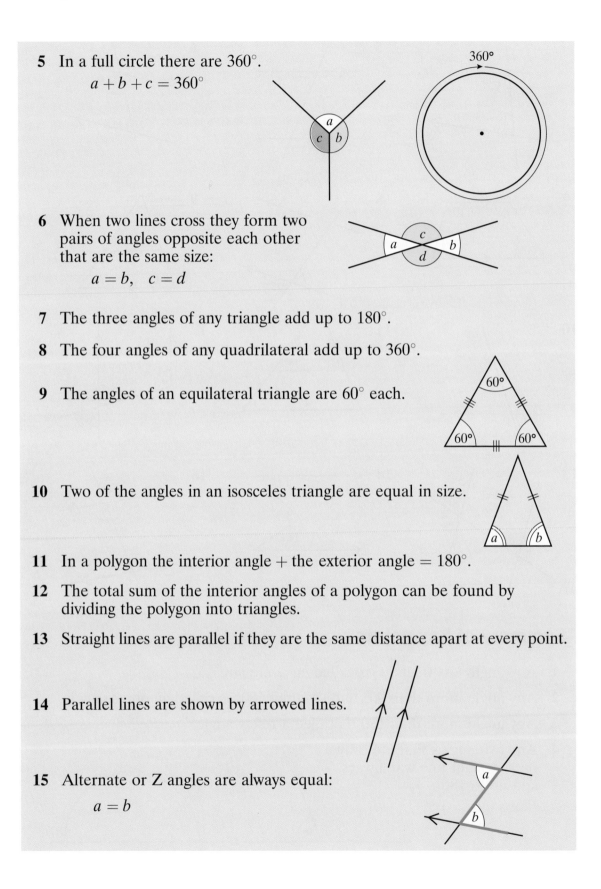

5 In a full circle there are 360°.

$$a + b + c = 360°$$

360°

6 When two lines cross they form two pairs of angles opposite each other that are the same size:

$$a = b, \quad c = d$$

7 The three angles of any triangle add up to 180°.

8 The four angles of any quadrilateral add up to 360°.

9 The angles of an equilateral triangle are 60° each.

10 Two of the angles in an isosceles triangle are equal in size.

11 In a polygon the interior angle + the exterior angle = 180°.

12 The total sum of the interior angles of a polygon can be found by dividing the polygon into triangles.

13 Straight lines are parallel if they are the same distance apart at every point.

14 Parallel lines are shown by arrowed lines.

15 Alternate or Z angles are always equal:

$$a = b$$

16 Corresponding or F angles are always equal:

$c = d$

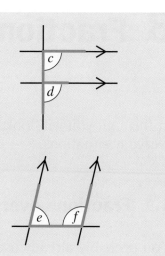

17 Supplementary or C angles add up to $180°$:

$e + f = 180°$

3 Fractions and ratio

In this unit you will look at the ways you use fractions in everyday situations.

3.1 Fractions everywhere

You probably already use fractions to describe many everyday situations.

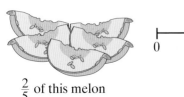

$\frac{2}{5}$ of this melon will be eaten

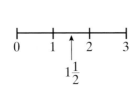

$1\frac{1}{2}$

Paul and his friends each get one and one third $\left(1\frac{1}{3}\right)$ of an apple pie. $1\frac{1}{3}$ can also be written as $\frac{4}{3}$.

- **A mixed number has a whole number part and a fraction part.**

- **Improper fractions are those in which the numerator is greater than the denominator. Improper fractions are also called top heavy fractions.**

The number on top is called the numerator

$\frac{3}{4}$

The number at the bottom is called the denominator

Sophie brought three cherry tarts to share with Paul and his friends. The three tarts were shared between four people. Each person gets one quarter of each of the three tarts. So each person gets $3 \div 4$ or $\frac{3}{4}$ of a tart.

- **A fraction can be expressed as a division.**

Samina joined the party. She brought a bag of 35 sweets which she shared between the five of them.

$$\tfrac{1}{5} \text{ of } 35 = 35 \div 5 = 7$$

One person did not want any sweets so Paul had an extra share. Paul had $\tfrac{2}{5}$ of the 35 sweets.

To find $\tfrac{2}{5}$ of 35.

$\tfrac{1}{5}$ of $35 = 35 \div 5 = 7$

   2 lots is $2 \times 7 = 14$

So $\tfrac{2}{5}$ of 35 is 14

To find a fifth of an amount you divide by 5.
To find two fifths $\left(\tfrac{2}{5}\right)$ of an amount you divide by 5 then multiply your answer by 2.

Example 1

Find $\tfrac{2}{5}$ of 120.
$\tfrac{1}{5}$ of $120 = 120 \div 5 = 24$
2 lots of $24 = 2 \times 24 = 48$

Example 2

Find $\tfrac{3}{10}$ of an hour.

There are 60 minutes in 1 hour.
So $\tfrac{1}{10}$ of 60 minutes $= 60 \div 10 = 6$ minutes
 3 lots of 6 minutes $= 3 \times 6 = 18$ minutes

Exercise 3A

1 Match up the following numbers into pairs of proper and improper fractions.

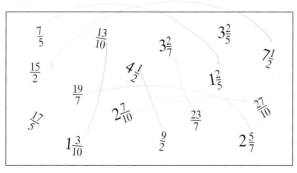

For example:

$$3\tfrac{2}{5} = \tfrac{17}{5}$$

2 Find the following:

(a) $\frac{1}{6}$ of 72 (b) $\frac{1}{4}$ of 216 metres

(c) $\frac{1}{8}$ of 96 kg (d) $\frac{7}{10}$ of 1000 g

(e) $\frac{2}{7}$ of £42 (f) $\frac{5}{12}$ of 24 pencils

3 Find the following (you may need to use the box to help you):

(a) $\frac{5}{6}$ of 3 dozen eggs (b) $\frac{2}{3}$ of 4 hours

(c) $\frac{3}{5}$ of 4 metres (d) $\frac{3}{20}$ of 2 kg

(e) $\frac{3}{8}$ of 4 minutes (f) $\frac{2}{25}$ of 3 FF

Remember:

1 hour = 60 minutes

1 minute = 60 seconds

one dozen = 12

1 metre
    = 100 centimetres

1 kg = 1000 g

1 French franc (FF)
    = 100 centimes

4 Karen walked $1\frac{2}{5}$ km. How far is this in metres?

5 A casserole takes $2\frac{3}{4}$ hours to cook. Write this time in minutes.

6 At a football match $\frac{2}{3}$ of the 12 000 supporters bought their tickets before the day of the match and a quarter of these people were under 18.

(a) How many supporters bought their tickets before the day of the match?

(b) How many of those who bought their tickets before the day of the match were under 18?

(c) How many supporters bought their tickets on the day of the match?

(d) Of the supporters who bought their tickets on the day of the match, $\frac{2}{5}$ were women. How many women bought their tickets on the day of the match?

3.2 Equivalent fractions

You can multiply or divide the top and bottom numbers of a fraction:

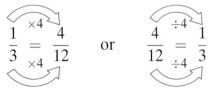

$\frac{1}{3}$ and $\frac{4}{12}$ are **equivalent fractions**, that means they have the same value.

■ **Equivalent fractions represent the same value.**

■ **Equivalent fractions can be found by multiplying or dividing the top and bottom of a fraction by the same number.**

We use equivalent fractions when adding and subtracting fractions, and to compare the size of fractions.

Example 3

Find equivalent fractions for $\frac{2}{3}$.

$$\frac{2}{3} \boxed{\begin{array}{l} 2 \times 4 \text{ is } 8 \\ 3 \times 4 \text{ is } 12 \end{array}} \frac{8}{12} \qquad \frac{2}{3} \boxed{\begin{array}{l} 2 \times 5 \text{ is } 10 \\ 3 \times 5 \text{ is } 15 \end{array}} \frac{10}{15}$$

so $\quad \frac{2}{3} = \frac{8}{12} = \frac{10}{15}$

Example 4

Find equivalent fractions for $\frac{21}{42}$.

$$\frac{21}{42} \boxed{\begin{array}{l} 21 \div 3 \text{ is } 7 \\ 42 \div 3 \text{ is } 14 \end{array}} \frac{7}{14} \boxed{\begin{array}{l} 7 \div 7 \text{ is } 1 \\ 14 \div 7 \text{ is } 2 \end{array}} \frac{1}{2}$$

so $\quad \frac{21}{42} = \frac{7}{14} = \frac{1}{2}$

Exercise 3B

1 Find sets of equivalent fractions in the box below.

$$\frac{1}{2} \qquad \frac{12}{18} \qquad \frac{15}{20} \qquad \frac{25}{50}$$
$$\frac{18}{27}$$
$$\frac{3}{4} \qquad \qquad \frac{27}{54} \qquad \frac{6}{9} \qquad \frac{9}{18}$$
$$\frac{9}{12}$$

2 Find an equivalent fraction for $\frac{5}{13}$
   (a) with a denominator of 39
   (b) with a numerator of 26
   (c) with a denominator of 52.

3 Find all the equivalent fractions for $\frac{42}{63}$ that have a denominator less than 63.

3.3 Simplifying fractions

$\frac{3}{4}, \frac{6}{8}, \frac{9}{12}$ and $\frac{45}{60}$ are all equivalent fractions.

They all have the same value.

$\frac{3}{4}$ is the simplest form of this set of fractions because there is no common factor of 3 or 4 that is greater than 1.

Simplifying fractions is sometimes called cancelling.

- ■ **Fractions can be simplified if the numerator and the denominator have a common factor greater than 1.**

- ■ **To find the simplest form of a fraction divide both the numerator and the denominator by the highest common factor.**

Example 5

Reduce the following fractions to their simplest forms:

(a) $\frac{30}{45}$ **(b)** $\frac{48}{60}$

(a) Factors of 30 are 1, 2, 3, 5, 6, 15 and 30
    Factors of 45 are 1, 3, 5, 9, 15 and 45

    The highest common factor of 30 and 45 is 15

$$\frac{30}{45} \quad \xrightarrow[{45 \,\div\, 15}]{{30 \,\div\, 15}} \quad \frac{2}{3}$$

    The simplest form of $\frac{30}{45}$ is $\frac{2}{3}$.

(b) The highest common factor of 48 and 60 is 12

$$\frac{48}{60} \quad \xrightarrow[{60 \,\div\, 12}]{{48 \,\div\, 12}} \quad \frac{4}{5}$$

    The simplest form of $\frac{48}{60}$ is $\frac{4}{5}$.

A fraction can also be written in its simplest form by cancelling common factors. This is the same as dividing both the numerator and the denominator by the same factor.

$\frac{12}{20}$ is the same as $\frac{4 \times 3}{4 \times 5}$ $\frac{15}{24}$ is the same as $\frac{3 \times 5}{3 \times 4 \times 2}$

The highest common factor is 4,   The only common factor is 3, so the simplest form of $\frac{12}{20}$ is $\frac{3}{5}$ so the simplest form of $\frac{15}{24}$ is $\frac{5}{8}$

Exercise 3C

1 Write the following fractions in their simplest forms by cancelling the highest common factors.

(a) $\frac{5}{35}$ (b) $\frac{13}{39}$ (c) $\frac{28}{63}$ (d) $\frac{75}{125}$

2 Cancel the following fractions to find their simplest forms:

(a) $\frac{12}{18}$ (b) $\frac{140}{420}$ (c) $\frac{99}{132}$ (d) $\frac{48}{126}$

3 Which of the following fractions is the simplest form of $\frac{28}{42}$?

$$\frac{10}{15} \qquad \frac{4}{21} \qquad \frac{4}{7} \qquad \frac{2}{3} \qquad \frac{14}{21}$$

4 Janet and Colin both worked out the simplest form of the fraction $\frac{36}{135}$. Colin's answer was $\frac{4}{5}$. Janet's answer was $\frac{12}{45}$. Neither was correct.

(a) Work out your own answer.
(b) Explain Colin's mistake.
(c) What is wrong with Janet's answer?

3.4 Comparison of fractions

If two fractions have the same denominator, the fraction having the larger numerator is the bigger fraction.

Example 6

Which is the larger fraction

(a) $\frac{5}{8}$ or $\frac{3}{8}$?   (b) $\frac{1}{10}$ or $\frac{9}{10}$?

(a) $\frac{5}{8}$ is larger since $5 > 3$ (b) $\frac{9}{10}$ is larger since $9 > 1$

$<$ means **less than**, so $2 < 5$ reads as '2 is less than 5'

$>$ means **greater than**, so $7 > 1$ reads as '7 is greater than 1'

To compare fractions with different denominators, you need to find equivalent fractions with the same denominator.

Example 7

Which fraction is the greater in each pair?

(a) $\frac{1}{3}$ and $\frac{5}{6}$ 　　　　　　　　　 **(b)** $5\frac{1}{2}$ and $\frac{7}{2}$

(a) $\overset{\times 2}{\underset{\times 2}{\frac{1}{3} = \frac{2}{6}}}$　so to compare $\frac{1}{3}$ and $\frac{5}{6}$ we rewrite the fractions as $\frac{2}{6}$ and $\frac{5}{6}$ we can now see that $\frac{2}{6} < \frac{5}{6}$, so $\frac{5}{6}$ is greater than $\frac{1}{3}$.

(b) To compare $5\frac{1}{2}$ and $\frac{7}{2}$, we rewrite the fractions as $5\frac{1}{2}$ and $3\frac{1}{2}$, $5\frac{1}{2} > 3\frac{1}{2}$, so $5\frac{1}{2}$ is greater than $\frac{7}{2}$.

Example 8

Write these fractions in ascending order:

$$\frac{1}{4}, \quad \frac{4}{9}, \quad \frac{5}{12}$$

To compare $\frac{1}{4}$, $\frac{4}{9}$ and $\frac{5}{12}$ we need to make these fractions into equivalent fractions with the same denominator:

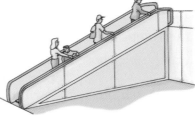

$$\frac{1}{4}, \frac{4}{9}, \frac{5}{12} \text{ are equivalent to } \frac{9}{36}, \frac{16}{36}, \frac{15}{36}$$

In ascending order: $\frac{9}{36}, \frac{15}{36}, \frac{16}{36}$

So in ascending order the original fractions are: $\frac{1}{4}, \frac{5}{12}, \frac{4}{9}$.

Exercise 3D

1 Use $<$ and $>$ to put the following pairs of fractions in order.

(a) $\frac{1}{2} \square \frac{5}{16}$ 　　　**(b)** $\frac{8}{16} \square \frac{3}{4}$ 　　　**(c)** $\frac{9}{12} \square \frac{2}{3}$

(d) $\frac{5}{6} \square \frac{7}{12}$ 　　　**(e)** $\frac{2}{5} \square \frac{3}{10}$

2 Change the following fractions so that they all have the same denominator. Then arrange them in descending order so that the largest fraction is written first.

$$\frac{3}{4} \quad \frac{5}{6}, \quad \frac{5}{8}, \quad \frac{1}{9}$$

3 Arrange the following fractions in ascending order:

$$\frac{2}{3}, \quad \frac{3}{4}, \quad \frac{5}{2}, \quad \frac{5}{8}$$

3.5 Decimal fractions

Fractions whose denominators are 10, 100, 1000, etc. can be written as decimals.

$\frac{1}{10}$ is the same as 0.1

$\frac{3}{10}$ is the same as 0.3

$\frac{1}{100}$ is the same as 0.01

$\frac{5}{100}$ is the same as 0.05

$\frac{1}{1000}$ is the same as 0.001

$\frac{13}{1000}$ is the same as 0.013

10 is 10^1 $\frac{1}{10}$ is 10^{-1}

100 is 10^2 $\frac{1}{100}$ is 10^{-2}

1000 is 10^3 $\frac{1}{1000}$ is 10^{-3}

You can find the decimal equivalent of a fraction by changing its denominator to 10, 100, 1000, etc.

■ **A fraction can be changed into a decimal by finding the equivalent fraction with a denominator of 10, 100, 1000 etc.**

Example 9

Change $\frac{7}{20}$ to a decimal.

$\frac{7}{20}$ is the same as $\frac{35}{100}$

$\frac{35}{100} = 0.35$

so the decimal equivalent of $\frac{7}{20}$ is 0.35.

You can also find the decimal equivalent of a fraction by dividing its numerator by its denominator.

You can also use your calculator to change fractions into decimals by dividing the numerator by the denominator.

$\frac{1}{5}$ means $1 \div 5$

$\frac{3}{20}$ means $3 \div 20$

so $\frac{1}{5} = 0.2$

so $\frac{3}{20} = 0.15$

■ **Fractions can also be changed into decimals by dividing the numerator by the denominator.**

Example 10

(a) Write the following fractions in words:

$$\frac{3}{10}, \qquad \frac{16}{100}$$

(b) Change these fractions to decimals.

(a) Three tenths, sixteen hundredths

(b) 0.3, 0.16

Example 11

Change the fraction $\frac{3}{4}$ to a decimal.

$\frac{3}{4}$ means $3 \div 4$

$$\begin{array}{r} 0.75 \\ 4\overline{)3.^30^20} \end{array}$$

so $\frac{3}{4}$ is the same as 0.75.

There is more about dividing with decimals on page 84.

Exercise 3E

1   Write the following fractions as decimals:
   (a) $\frac{7}{10}$ (b) $\frac{23}{100}$ (c) $2\frac{3}{10}$ (d) $\frac{149}{1000}$

2   By finding equivalent fractions, change the following fractions into decimals:
   (a) $\frac{4}{5}$ (b) $\frac{6}{2000}$ (c) $\frac{58}{20}$ (d) $\frac{609}{30000}$

3   Write each fraction as a division sum and change it into a decimal.
   (a) $\frac{3}{4}$ (b) $\frac{5}{8}$ (c) $\frac{5}{16}$
   (d) $3\frac{1}{8}$ (e) $\frac{2}{3}$ (f) $5\frac{1}{4}$

   What do you notice about answer (e)? Can you explain why this happens?

4   Change the following fractions into decimals:
   (a) $\frac{7}{16}$ (b) $\frac{7}{40}$ (c) $\frac{11}{125}$ (d) $\frac{120}{80}$

3.6 Adding and subtracting fractions

■ **To add or subtract fractions find equivalent fractions fractions that have the same denominator.**

Example 12

Add $\frac{3}{8}$ and $\frac{1}{3}$.

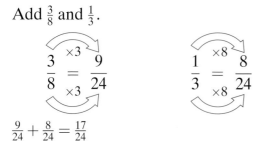

$$\frac{3}{8} \xrightarrow{\times 3} \frac{9}{24} \qquad \frac{1}{3} \xrightarrow{\times 8} \frac{8}{24}$$

$$\frac{9}{24} + \frac{8}{24} = \frac{17}{24}$$

Example 13

Subtract $\frac{1}{4}$ from $\frac{1}{3}$.

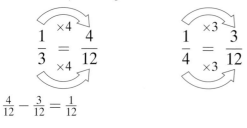

$$\frac{1}{3} \xrightarrow{\times 4} \frac{4}{12} \qquad \frac{1}{4} \xrightarrow{\times 3} \frac{3}{12}$$

$$\frac{4}{12} - \frac{3}{12} = \frac{1}{12}$$

3.7 Adding and subtracting mixed numbers

To add mixed numbers you must first add the whole numbers, then add the fraction parts. You can then add the mixed numbers together.

Example 14

Add $3\frac{3}{4}$ and $1\frac{1}{8}$.

First add the whole numbers: $3 + 1 = 4$

Then add the fractions: $\frac{3}{4} + \frac{1}{8}$

$$\frac{3}{4} \xrightarrow{\times 2} \frac{6}{8}, \quad \text{so} \quad \frac{6}{8} + \frac{1}{8} = \frac{7}{8}$$

$$3\frac{3}{4} + 1\frac{1}{8} = 4\frac{7}{8}$$

Example 15

Subtract one and two sevenths from three and a half.

First subtract the whole numbers: $3 - 1 = 2$

Then subtract the fractions: $\frac{1}{2} - \frac{2}{7}$

$$\frac{1}{2} \overset{\times 7}{\underset{\times 7}{=}} \frac{7}{14} \qquad \frac{2}{7} \overset{\times 2}{\underset{\times 2}{=}} \frac{4}{14}, \quad \text{so} \quad \frac{7}{14} - \frac{4}{14} = \frac{3}{14}$$

$$3\tfrac{1}{2} - 1\tfrac{2}{7} = 2\tfrac{3}{14}$$

Example 16

Find $1\tfrac{3}{12} - \tfrac{3}{4}$.

$$\frac{3}{4} \overset{\times 3}{\underset{\times 3}{=}} \frac{9}{12}$$

$$1\tfrac{3}{12} - \tfrac{3}{4} = 1\tfrac{3}{12} - \tfrac{9}{12}$$

You cannot subtract the fractions as $\frac{3}{12}$ is smaller than $\frac{9}{12}$.

You must change $1\tfrac{3}{12}$ into an improper fraction

$$1\tfrac{3}{12} = \tfrac{12}{12} + \tfrac{3}{12} = \tfrac{15}{12}$$

so $1\tfrac{3}{12} - \tfrac{9}{12} = \tfrac{15}{12} - \tfrac{9}{12} = \tfrac{6}{12} = \tfrac{1}{2}$

You should write your answer in its simplest form.

Exercise 3F

1 Find the sum of the following fractions:

   (a) $\frac{5}{6}$ and $\frac{3}{4}$ (b) $2\frac{1}{3}$ and $\frac{4}{15}$ (c) $1\frac{2}{3}$ and $2\frac{1}{4}$

   (d) $\frac{9}{5}$ and $\frac{1}{10}$ (e) $\frac{7}{12}$, $\frac{5}{8}$ and $1\frac{5}{6}$ (f) $\frac{5}{8}$ and $1\frac{1}{3}$

   (g) $\frac{15}{6}$ and $\frac{7}{9}$

2 Find the difference between the following fractions:

   (a) $\frac{5}{6}$ and $\frac{1}{4}$ (b) $\frac{11}{24}$ and $\frac{3}{8}$ (c) $3\frac{1}{2}$ and $1\frac{1}{4}$

   (d) $2\frac{1}{4}$ and $1\frac{2}{3}$ (e) $\frac{9}{5}$ and $\frac{1}{10}$ (f) $1\frac{7}{3}$ and $\frac{7}{6}$

3 Chi won some money in a raffle. He decided to give one ninth of it to the Animal Welfare fund. He gave a quarter to his sister and he saved $\frac{5}{18}$. What fraction did he have left to spend?

4 Amy took home her first paycheck. She had paid $\frac{1}{5}$ of her wage in tax, $\frac{1}{20}$ in National Insurance and $\frac{1}{10}$ into her pension fund. What fraction did she have left?

5 Hannah and Simon ran a 100 metre race. Hannah took $18\frac{1}{5}$ seconds and Simon took $21\frac{3}{4}$ seconds. How much longer did Simon take?

3.8 Multiplying fractions

Sophie and Paul were sharing a bar of chocolate. They each took one half of the bar. Amarjita arrived and asked Paul for a share of his chocolate. He gave her one third of his part, so she had one third of a half of the whole bar. Amarjita had one sixth of the bar.

We can look at this another way by writing

$\frac{1}{3}$ of $\frac{1}{2}$ as $\frac{1}{3} \times \frac{1}{2}$

$\frac{1}{3} \times \frac{1}{2} = \frac{1}{6}$

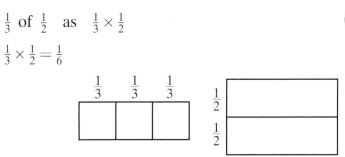

If Paul had given Amarjita $\frac{2}{3}$ of his chocolate she would have had $\frac{2}{3}$ of $\frac{1}{2}$ of the bar.

$\frac{2}{3}$ of $\frac{1}{2}$ is $\frac{2}{3} \times \frac{1}{2}$

$\frac{2}{3} \times \frac{1}{2} = \frac{2}{6}$ $\left(\text{or } \frac{1}{3}\right)$

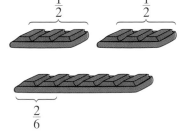

This is $\frac{2}{3}$ of $\frac{1}{2}$ the bar of chocolate, which is $\frac{2}{6}$ of the whole bar

■ **To multiply fractions, multiply the numerators together and multiply the denominators together. Then simplify the new fraction if possible.**

$$\frac{3}{8} \times \frac{2}{7} = \frac{3 \times 2}{8 \times 7} = \frac{6}{56}$$

$$\frac{6}{56} \overset{\div 2}{\underset{\div 2}{=}} \frac{3}{28}$$

so $\dfrac{3}{8} \times \dfrac{2}{7} = \dfrac{3}{28}$, writing the answer in its simplest form

■ **To multiply improper fractions, multiply their numerators and denominators together. Then simplify the new fraction if possible.**

$$\frac{6}{5} \times \frac{15}{8} = \frac{6 \times 15}{5 \times 8} = \frac{90}{40}$$

$$\frac{90}{40} \overset{\div 10}{\underset{\div 10}{=}} \frac{9}{4} = \frac{4}{4} + \frac{4}{4} + \frac{1}{4} = 2\frac{1}{4}$$

■ **To multiply mixed numbers, first change them into improper fractions and then multiply the improper fractions together.**

$$2\frac{2}{7} \times 1\frac{1}{4}$$

Change to improper fractions: $\dfrac{16}{7} \times \dfrac{5}{4}$

Multiply the two fractions: $\dfrac{16 \times 5}{7 \times 4}$

Simplify if possible: $\dfrac{80}{28} \overset{\div 4}{\underset{\div 4}{=}} \dfrac{20}{7} = 2\dfrac{6}{7}$

Example 17

Find $\frac{3}{5}$ of $\frac{5}{8}$.

$$\frac{3}{5} \text{ of } \frac{5}{8} = \frac{3}{5} \times \frac{5}{8} = \frac{3 \times 5}{5 \times 8}$$

$$= \frac{15}{40}$$

$$= \frac{3}{8}$$

This can also be shown using squares:

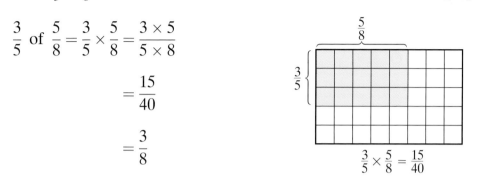

$$\frac{3}{5} \times \frac{5}{8} = \frac{15}{40}$$

Example 18

Find $2\frac{1}{2} \times 1\frac{1}{5}$.

First change to improper fractions: $\dfrac{5}{2} \times \dfrac{6}{5}$

Multiply the two fractions: $\dfrac{5 \times 6}{2 \times 5} = \dfrac{30}{10}$

Simplify: $\dfrac{30}{10} = \dfrac{3}{1} = 3$ (÷10)

3.9 Multiplying a fraction by a whole number

To multiply $\frac{4}{5}$ by 3 we can write 3 as the improper fraction $\frac{3}{1}$.

$$\frac{4}{5} \times \frac{3}{1} = \frac{4 \times 3}{5 \times 1} = \frac{12}{5} = \frac{5}{5} + \frac{5}{5} + \frac{2}{5} = 2\frac{2}{5}$$

Example 19

Find 5 times $\frac{2}{13}$

$$5 = \frac{5}{1} \quad \text{so} \quad \frac{5}{1} \times \frac{2}{13} = \frac{5 \times 2}{1 \times 13} = \frac{10}{13}$$

Exercise 3G

1 Work out:

(a) $\frac{1}{3} \times \frac{3}{5}$ (b) $\frac{3}{8} \times \frac{1}{6}$ (c) $\frac{2}{5} \times \frac{3}{5}$

(d) $\frac{7}{10} \times \frac{3}{8}$ (e) $\frac{5}{12} \times \frac{9}{14}$

2 Work out:

(a) $2 \times \frac{1}{7}$ (b) $4 \times \frac{4}{5}$ (c) $\frac{3}{8} \times 7$

(d) $\frac{5}{6} \times 11$ (e) $7 \times \frac{8}{15}$

3 Work out:

(a) $2\frac{1}{4} \times \frac{1}{3}$ (b) $\frac{2}{5} \times 3\frac{1}{2}$ (c) $2\frac{1}{3} \times 1\frac{1}{2}$

(d) $1\frac{5}{6} \times 1\frac{2}{3}$ (e) $3\frac{3}{4} \times 2\frac{1}{2}$

4 Find the missing number in each of the following:

(a) $\boxed{} \times \frac{1}{6} = \frac{5}{6}$ (b) $\boxed{} \times \frac{2}{7} = \frac{6}{7}$

(c) $5 \times \boxed{} = \frac{15}{7}$ (d) $\boxed{} \times 7 = 1\frac{2}{5}$

5 If $\frac{4}{5} = x \times \frac{1}{5}$, what is x?

6 If $\frac{8}{9} = 4 \times \dfrac{a}{9}$, what is a?

7 Find the value of each letter. In each case check your answer.

(a) $b \times 7 = \frac{7}{10}$ (b) $\frac{3}{10} \times y = \frac{9}{10}$

(c) $4 \times \dfrac{n}{9} = \dfrac{8}{9}$

8 Work out:

(a) $1\frac{1}{3} \times 2$ (b) $\left(3 \times \frac{1}{5}\right) + \left(3 \times \frac{2}{3}\right)$

(c) $\left(2 \times \frac{2}{5}\right) - \left(2 \times \frac{3}{10}\right)$

Remember to work out the calculation in the brackets first.

9 Helena has eight days for her holiday. She spends $\frac{2}{3}$ of the time on the beach. How many days of her holiday did she spend on the beach?

10 Mike has three bags of toffee. In each bag $\frac{3}{8}$ of the toffees are treacle. What fraction of all the toffee is treacle?

11 $\frac{1}{5}$ of a packet of muesli contains dried fruit. One third of the dried fruit is sultanas. What fraction of the muesli is sultanas?

12 Sixteen students went for a pizza. There was a special offer of "Eat one, get a half free". They all took advantage of the offer. How many pizzas did they eat?

13 A family goes to a theme park. The two grandparents pay $\frac{1}{3}$ of the full entrance price. The two parents pay full price and the three children pay half price. A full price ticket costs £5.70. How much was the total cost of admission for the family?

3.10 Dividing fractions

Here is a problem you can solve if you know how to divide fractions.

Trudie makes 3 kilograms of strawberry yoghurt, which she wants to put into yoghurt pots. Each yoghurt pot holds $\frac{1}{4}$ kilogram of yoghurt. How many pots will she need?

Trudie needs to divide her 3 kilograms of yoghurt into $\frac{1}{4}$ kilogram portions:

$$3 \div \tfrac{1}{4}$$

There are four quarters in a whole (i.e. in 1) so there are three lots of four quarters in the 3 kilograms of yoghurt.

$$3 \times 4 = 12$$

Trudie will need 12 pots for her yoghurt.

The reciprocal of 4 is $\frac{1}{4}$

The reciprocal of $\frac{1}{4}$ is 4

Christine has half of a Toblerone bar. She gives Tony $\frac{1}{3}$ of it. What fraction of a whole bar does Tony get?

Tony gets a third of half a bar,

$$\frac{1}{2} \times \frac{1}{3}$$

You can work this out by dividing $\frac{1}{2}$ by 3.

Dividing by 3 is the same as multiplying by $\frac{1}{3}$

so $\quad \frac{1}{2} \div 3 = \frac{1}{2} \times \frac{1}{3} = \frac{1}{6}$

Tony gets $\frac{1}{6}$ of the whole bar.

■ **To divide fractions turn the dividing fraction into its reciprocal and multiply.**

Example 20

Work out $\frac{3}{5} \div 7$

$$7 = \frac{7}{1}$$

so the reciprocal of 7 is $\frac{1}{7}$

so $\dfrac{3}{5} \div 7 = \dfrac{3}{5} \times \dfrac{1}{7}$

$\qquad = \dfrac{3 \times 1}{5 \times 7}$

$\qquad = \dfrac{3}{35}$

Example 21

Work out $\frac{2}{3} \div \frac{8}{9}$.

The reciprocal of $\dfrac{8}{9}$ is $\dfrac{9}{8}$

so $\dfrac{2}{3} \div \dfrac{8}{9} = \dfrac{2}{3} \times \dfrac{9}{8}$

$\qquad = \dfrac{2 \times 9}{3 \times 8}$

$\qquad = \dfrac{18}{24}$

$\qquad = \dfrac{3}{4}$

To find the reciprocal of a mixed number, first change it to an improper fraction, e.g.

$1\frac{2}{3} = \frac{5}{3}$

The reciprocal of

$\frac{5}{3}$ is $\frac{3}{5}$

Exercise 3H

1 Find the reciprocal for each fraction

  (a) $\frac{7}{9}$ **(b)** 12   **(c)** $\frac{1}{8}$ **(d)** $\frac{13}{8}$ **(e)** $1\frac{1}{7}$

2 Work out:

  (a) $\frac{1}{6} \div \frac{1}{5}$ **(b)** $\frac{3}{5} \div \frac{2}{3}$ **(c)** $\frac{5}{8} \div \frac{3}{4}$

3 Work out:

(a) $\frac{3}{5} \div 7$ (b) $\frac{9}{11} \div 6$ (c) $\frac{7}{15} \div 5$

4 Work out:

(a) $4 \div \frac{2}{5}$ (b) $6 \div \frac{1}{3}$ (c) $7 \div \frac{1}{12}$

5 Uncle Richie gave Wendy £120 to share with her brothers and sisters. Wendy decided to take half for herself and then gave half of what was left to Peter.

(a) How much did Wendy and Peter get each?

(b) What fraction of the whole amount did Peter get?

Wendy then shared the remaining amount between Timothy, Michael and Rotna. She gave half of the amount left to Timothy, then half of the remainder to Michael and then half of the rest to Rotna.

(c) How much did Timothy, Michael and Rotna get each?

(d) What fraction of the whole amount did each get?

(e) Explain the fraction pattern in these answers.

6

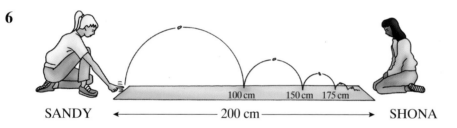

SANDY   ←————— 200 cm —————→   SHONA

Look at the picture above. Sandy and Shona are playing a game. Sandy flicks a coin so that it lands half-way between herself and Shona. She flicks it again and it lands half-way again. She continues this pattern.

(a) How many flicks will it take for the coin to reach Shona?

(b) Does the distance between Shona and Sandy affect the number of flicks the coin will take?

7 Match the statements that give the same answer.

(a) $\frac{2}{3}$ of 45   (b) $45 \div \frac{2}{3}$ (c) $1\frac{1}{2} \times 45$

(d) $\frac{2}{3} \times 45$ (e) $45 \div \frac{3}{2}$ (f) $45 \div 1\frac{1}{2}$

3.11 Fractions and ratio

Look at the diagram below. The circle is divided into eight parts.

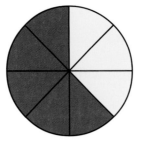

Three parts are yellow and five parts are red.

Describing this in fractions we would say that

$\frac{3}{8}$ of the circle is yellow and $\frac{5}{8}$ of the circle is red.

However, in ratios we compare two quantities.

So in the circle above we would say there are three parts yellow to five parts red or that the ratio of yellow to red is 3 to 5.

This is written as 3 : 5.

We can also say that there are 5 parts red to 3 parts yellow or that the ratio of red to yellow is 5 to 3, written as 5 : 3.

Example 22

(a) What fraction of the rectangle is blue?
(b) What fraction of the rectangle is yellow?
(c) Write the ratio of blue parts to yellow parts.
(d) Write the ratio of yellow parts to blue parts.

(a) There are seven parts in the shape and three are blue, so $\frac{3}{7}$ of the rectangle is blue.

(b) There are seven parts in the shape and four are yellow, so $\frac{4}{7}$ of the rectangle is yellow.

(c) There are three blue parts to four yellow, so the ratio of blue to yellow is 3 to 4, written as 3 : 4.

(d) There are four yellow parts to three blue, so the ratio of yellow to blue is 4 to 3, written as 4 : 3.

Exercise 3I

For each of the diagrams below:

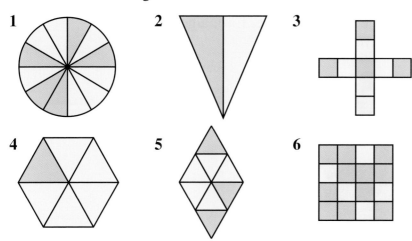

1 **2** **3**

4 **5** **6**

(a) What fraction of the shape is blue?
(b) What fraction of the shape is yellow?
(c) What is the ratio of blue parts to yellow parts?
(d) What is the ratio of yellow parts to blue parts?

3.12 Simplifying ratios

Ratios are equivalent when the relationship between each pair of numbers is the same. Look at the diagram.

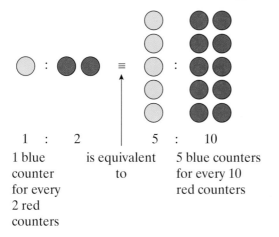

1 : 2		5 : 10
1 blue counter for every 2 red counters	is equivalent to	5 blue counters for every 10 red counters

For each blue counter there are two red counters, so the ratio of blue to red is 1 : 2.
This is equivalent to the ratio 5 : 10.

■ **To simplify a ratio divide the numbers in the ratio by a common factor.**

In the diagram below 32 sweets are shared in the ratio of 1 : 2 : 5. This means that Jane gets one share, Emma gets two shares and James gets five shares.

You can also describe this ratio as 4 : 8 : 20, as Jane has 4 sweets, Emma has 8 sweets and James has 20 sweets.

If the numbers in the ratio do not have a common factor then the ratio is in its simplest or lowest form.
We usually write ratios in their lowest form.

Numbers having a common factor can each be divided by that factor,
e.g. 3 is a common factor of 3, 12 and 27.

Example 23

Simplify the ratio 15 : 20 so that it is in its lowest form.

15 and 20 share a common factor of 5, so

$$
\begin{array}{cc}
15 : 20 \\
15 \div 5 \quad\downarrow \quad 20 \div 5 \\
3 \ : \ 4
\end{array}
$$

Example 24

Simplify 4 : 8 : 20.

$$
\begin{array}{ccc}
4 : 8 : 20 \\
4 \div 4 \quad 8 \div 4 \quad 20 \div 4 \\
1 : 2 : 5
\end{array}
$$

Example 25

Paul was counting his fish: he had 6 blue fish, 15 gold fish and 12 red fish.
Write this as a ratio in its lowest form.

First write the ratio describing the numbers of different fish, 6 : 15 : 12.

The largest number that divides into all three numbers (the highest common factor) is 3, so

$$6 : 15 : 12$$

$$6 \div 3 \quad | \quad 15 \div 3 \quad | \quad 12 \div 3$$

$$2 \ : \ 5 \ : \ 4$$

The ratio in its lowest form is 2 : 5 : 4

Exercise 3J

1 Write these ratios in their lowest form:

    (a)   3 : 6   **(b)**   6 : 18

    (c)   8 : 24   **(d)** 14 : 6

    (e) 64 : 16   **(f)**   5 : 10 : 15

    (g)   7 : 21 : 28   **(h)** 72 : 36 : 18

    (i) 52 : 39 : 13   **(j)**   9 : 20 : 35

2 Write these ratios in their lowest form.

    (a)   4 : 16   **(b)** 30 : 18

    (c) 14 : 49   **(d)**   2 : 6 : 12

    (e) 40 : 24 : 18   **(f)** 10 : 15 : 30

3 Jerry is sorting out his minidisc, DVD, tape and CD collections. He has 80 minidiscs, 16 DVDs, 96 CDs and 120 cassettes.

    (a) Write down the ratio of minidiscs to DVDs. Simplify your answer.

    (b) Write down the ratio of CDs to cassettes. Write your answer in its simplest form.

  (c) What is the ratio of minidiscs to CDs to DVDs?
      Simplify this if possible.

  (d) Write down the ratio of cassettes to CDs to
      minidiscs to DVDs.

4 Write each of the following ratios in its simplest form.
  Remember to make the units the same before you
  write each ratio.

  (a) 350 grams to 7 kg

  (b) 3 hours to 240 minutes

  (c) £5 to £1.40

  (d) 1 litre of milk to $\frac{1}{2}$ litre of milk

  (e) 8 years to 3 years 6 months

5 In a class there are 25 boys and 15 girls. Find the ratio of

  (a) boys to girls

  (b) girls to boys

  (c) boys to the total number of pupils

  (d) girls to the total number of pupils.

6 A librarian is sorting out books into fiction, non-fiction
  and reference. She has 120 non-fiction books,
  248 fiction books and 72 reference books.

  (a) Write down the ratio of fiction to non-fiction to
      reference.

  (b) Write down the ratio of reference to non-fiction.

  (c) Write down the ratios in parts (a) and (b) in their
      lowest forms.

7 Tony's garden has 81 snowdrops, 36 crocuses and
  90 daffodils.

  (a) Write down the ratio of snowdrops to daffodils to
      crocuses.

  (b) Write down the ratio of daffodils to snowdrops in
      its lowest form.

  (c) Write down the ratio of crocuses to snowdrops to
      daffodils in its lowest form.

8 Pierre's recipe uses 42 spoons of flour to 12 spoons of cocoa.

   (a) Write down the ratio of cocoa to flour.

   (b) If Pierre uses seven spoons of flour how many spoons of cocoa will he need?

   (c) He decides to use 18 spoons of cocoa. How many spoons of flour does he need?

9 Superduper market gives four free drinks with every six multipacks of crisps bought.

   (a) Write down the ratio of drinks to multipacks of crisps in the lowest form.

   (b) If I buy 12 multipacks of crisps, how many free drinks will I get?

   (c) Diana wants 14 free drinks, how many multipacks must she buy?

   (d) If Diana wants seven free drinks, can she use the offer?

3.13 Using ratios as scales

Scale diagrams are often used in house plans, in instructions for assembling furniture and in maps to represent distances on the ground. Each length in the scale diagram represents a real length in the house, on the furniture or on the map.

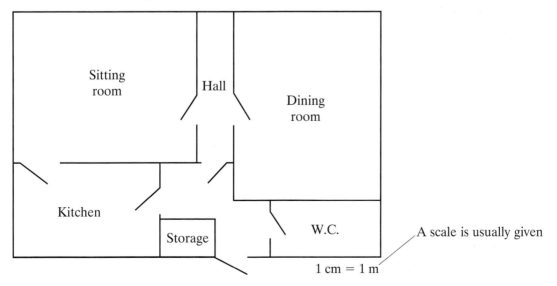

Example 26

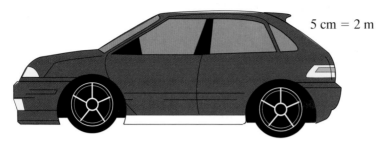

5 cm = 2 m

On the diagram 5 cm represents 2 metres.

What lengths do

(a) $\frac{1}{2}$ cm   (b) 4 cm represent?

    5 cm represents 2 metre or 200 cm

    1 cm represents $200 \div 5 = 40$ cm

(a) $\frac{1}{2}$ cm represents $40 \text{ cm} \div 2 = 20$ cm

(b) 4 cm represents $4 \times 40 \text{ cm} = 160$ cm

Exercise 3K

1 Draw a scale plan of a garden in which 10 mm represents 1 metre. The garden is 5 metres long and 10 metres wide. A 1 metre wide path runs the length of the garden. In one half of the garden draw a pond with a diameter of 3 metres. Ask the person sitting next to you to check your drawing.

2 A mobile phone company uses a ratio of 1 : 2 for the drawing of a phone used in an advertisement. The height of the actual phone is 15 cm.

    (a) What height is the phone shown on the advertisement?

    (b) The width of the phone in the drawing is $2\frac{1}{2}$ cm. What is the width of the actual phone?

    (c) The aerial on the drawing of the phone is $1\frac{1}{2}$ cm high. What is the actual height of the aerial?

3 The Superscale Road Atlas uses a scale of 1 : 150 000.
The distance between Brigearn and Belton is
approximately 66 km.

1 : 150 000 means
1 cm on the map
represents
150 000 cm on the
ground.

   (a) How many metres are there in a kilometre?

   (b) How many centimetres are there in a kilometre?

   (c) How many centimetres are there in 66 kilometres?

   (d) What length on the map represents the distance
between Brigearn and Belton?

   (e) On the same map a length of 10 cm represents
David's daily journey to work. What is this actual
distance?

4 An architectural model for a temple uses
a scale of 1 : 50. The dimensions of the
model are approximately 90 cm, 60 cm and 40 cm.
Work out the dimensions of the actual temple.

5 A model of a child's cradle has a scale of 1 : 30. The
width of the model cradle is 3.5 cm. How wide would
the real cradle be?

Summary of key points

1 A mixed number has a whole number part and a
fraction part.

2 Improper fractions are those in which the numerator
is greater than the denominator. Improper fractions
are also called top heavy fractions.

3 A fraction can be expressed as a division sum.

4 Equivalent fractions represent the same value.

5 Equivalent fractions can be found by multiplying or
dividing the top and bottom of a fraction by the
same number.

6 Fractions can be simplified if the numerator and the
denominator have a common factor greater than 1.

7 To find the simplest form of a fraction divide both
the numerator and the denominator by the highest
common factor.

8 A fraction can be changed into a decimal by finding the equivalent fraction with a denominator of 10, 100, 1000, etc.

9 Fractions can also be changed into decimals by dividing the numerator by the denominator.

10 To add or subtract fractions find equivalent fractions that have the same denominator.

11 To multiply fractions, multiply the numerators together and multiply the denominators together. Then simplify the new fraction if possible.

12 To multiply improper fractions, multiply their numerators and denominators together. Then simplify the new fraction if possible.

13 To multiply mixed numbers, first change them into improper fractions and then multiply the improper fractions together.

14 To divide fractions, turn the dividing fraction into its reciprocal and multiply.

15 To simplify a ratio divide the numbers in the ratio by a common factor.

4 Probability

A

B

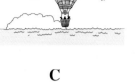

C

This balloon is unlikely to fly around the world.

There is a fifty-fifty chance of this balloon crossing the Pacific.

It is likely that this balloon will land in the sea.

4.1 What is probability?

Probability is a measure of how likely something is to happen.

The balloon in picture **B** has an even chance of crossing the Pacific.

The balloon in picture **A** is unlikely to fly around the world.

The balloon in picture **C** is likely to land in the sea.

The chance, or likelihood, of these and other outcomes happening can be shown on the likelihood scale:

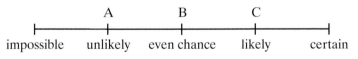

You can also mark the probability of an outcome happening on a probability scale.

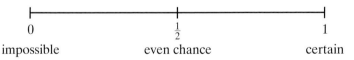

An outcome that is unlikely to occur has a probability between 0 and $\frac{1}{2}$.

An outcome that is likely to occur has a probability between $\frac{1}{2}$ and 1.

Find out how Pascal, Fermat, Huygens and Bernoulli all contributed to the Theory of Probability in the 17th century.

Probabilities can be written as fractions, decimals or percentages:

$\frac{1}{2} = 0.5 = 50\%$

- **Probability uses numbers to measure the chance of an outcome happening.**

- **An outcome that is certain to happen has a probability of 1.**

- **An outcome that cannot happen has a probability of 0.**

- **All probabilities have a value from 0 to 1.**

Example 1

Mark each of these outcomes on a probability scale.
Give a reason for your answer.

(a) A family living in the city will own a boat.

(b) When you throw a coin it will land as a head.

(c) It will get dark in Manchester tonight.

(d) It will rain this month in London.

(e) You will be a year younger next year.

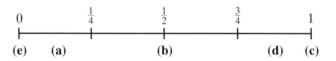

(a) This is unlikely as very few people living in cities will own a boat.

(b) A coin has an even chance of landing on a head.

(c) It is certain to get dark in Manchester at some time during the night.

(d) It is very likely to rain in any month in London.

(e) It is impossible for anybody to be a year younger the following year.

Exercise 4A

Draw a probability scale and mark the numbers $0, \frac{1}{4}, \frac{1}{2}, \frac{3}{4}$ and 1 on it. Mark the following outcomes on your scale giving a reason for your answer.

(a) There will be a power cut this evening.

(b) You will have a hair cut this year.

(c) You will get an even number when you throw a dice.

(d) You will play football this week.

(e) You will listen to classical music today.

4.2 Calculating probabilities

You can calculate the probability of an event happening.
Some events have equally likely outcomes.

When you throw a 10-sided die,
there are 10 possible outcomes.
They are all equally likely.

One of these outcomes is the number 7.
There is a 1 in 10 chance of getting a 7.
The probability of getting a 7 can be written as

$$\text{Probability } (7) = \tfrac{1}{10}$$

or $\quad P(7) = \tfrac{1}{10}$

There are five odd numbers between 1 and 10.
The probability of getting an odd number can be written as

$$P(\text{odd}) = \tfrac{5}{10}$$

■ **The probability that something will happen is**

$$P(\text{event}) = \frac{\text{the number of successful outcomes}}{\text{the total number of possible outcomes}}$$

Example 2

(a) On the 10-sided die what is the probability of
getting an integer?

(b) What is the probability of getting a fraction?

(c) What is the probability of getting a number greater
than 5?

(d) What is the probability of getting a 5?

(e) What is the probability of getting the numbers 1, 2, 3 or 4?

(f) Add the three fractions in parts **(c)**, **(d)** and **(e)**.
What do you notice?

Remember:
an integer is a
whole number.

(a) 1 because all the numbers are integers.

(b) 0 because none of the numbers are fractions.

(c) $\tfrac{5}{10}$ because there are five numbers greater than 5.

(d) $\tfrac{1}{10}$ as there is only one chance of getting a 5.

(e) $\tfrac{4}{10}$

(f) $\tfrac{5}{10} + \tfrac{1}{10} + \tfrac{4}{10} = \tfrac{10}{10}$. The probabilities add up to 1.

Example 3

One of these computer disks has a virus.

(a) What is the probability of choosing the disk with the virus?

(b) What is the probability of choosing a disk without a virus?

(a) $\frac{1}{4}$ (b) $\frac{3}{4}$

Exercise 4B

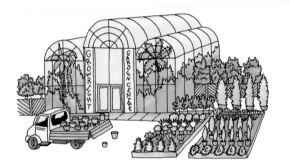

1 Five different bulbs have been placed in a bag. One bulb is a yellow daffodil, one is a purple crocus, one is a white snowdrop, one is a white lily and one is a red tulip.

(a) A bulb is picked from the bag without looking. What is the probability that a tulip bulb is picked from the bag?

(b) What is the probability that a bulb picked from the bag will grow into a white flower?

(c) What is the probability that a bulb picked from the bag will produce a flower that is not yellow?

(d) What is the probability that a bulb picked from the bag will produce a flower that is not white?

2 David delivers pots to the Grow Right garden centre. There are 10 white ceramic pots, 10 blue ceramic pots, 5 terracotta pots, 20 white plastic pots, 5 blue plastic pots and 50 green plastic pots. He removes these pots from his van randomly.

(a) What is the probability that he takes out a blue plastic pot?

(b) What is the probability that he takes out a plastic pot?

(c) What is the probability that he takes out a ceramic pot?

(d) What is the probability that he takes out a terracotta pot?

(e) What is the probability that he takes out a pot that is not ceramic?

3 There are two yellow and three green wheelbarrows in the garden centre. Toby picks up a wheelbarrow without looking. What is the probability that Toby will use:

(a) a yellow wheelbarrow

(b) a green wheelbarrow

(c) a red wheelbarrow?

4 Toby wants to eat fruit at lunch time. He picks an item from the fruit bowl without looking. What is the probability that he takes:

(a) an apple   **(b)** a banana

(c) a pear   **(d)** a green fruit

(e) an orange?

5 In the seed packet section of the store there are 200 packets of pea seeds, 150 packets of green bean seeds and some packets of carrot seeds. One of the packets is damaged. The probability that the damaged packet is of pea seeds is $\frac{200}{1000}$.

(a) How many packets of seeds are there in total?

(b) What is the probability of the damaged packet containing carrot seeds?

6 A stall at the local fete has numbers from 1 to 100 in a drum. It costs 10p to pick a number. If the number is a multiple of 15 you get your money back. If the number is a prime number less than 30 you get double your money back. All the numbers are always returned to the drum. Yvonne picks a number. Find the probability that she

(a) gets her 10p back   **(b)** wins an extra 10p.

7   At the next stall a magician is showing card tricks.
   The magician is trying to guess the card that Peter
   has chosen from an ordinary pack of playing cards.
   Find the probability that the magician will be
   correct if she says it is

   (a) a black card   **(b)** a diamond

   (c) the seven of clubs   **(d)** a red two

   (e) a picture card   **(f)** a red picture card.

4.3 Probabilities adding up to one

In the picture above the baby can choose any one of the
10 shapes. This means there are 10 equally likely outcomes.

There are three triangles, so the probability
of choosing a triangle is P(triangle) $= \frac{3}{10}$.

There are four hexagons, so the probability
of choosing a hexagon is P(hexagon) $= \frac{4}{10}$.

There are three circles, so the probability
of choosing a circle is P(circle) $= \frac{3}{10}$.

$$\tfrac{3}{10} + \tfrac{4}{10} + \tfrac{3}{10} = \tfrac{10}{10} = 1$$

When a shape is chosen it must be either a triangle, a
hexagon or a circle. These are all the possible outcomes.
Because one of these shapes must be chosen, their
probabilities must add up to 1.

■   **The probabilities of all the possible outcomes of an
   event add up to 1.**

Example 4

The probability of picking a red cube from the bag is $\frac{5}{9}$.

The probability of picking a green cube is $\frac{1}{9}$.

There are only red, green and yellow cubes in the bag.

What is the probability of choosing a yellow cube?

$$P(\text{red}) = \frac{5}{9}$$
$$P(\text{green}) = \frac{1}{9}$$

The denominator tells us the number of possible outcomes.

$$\frac{9}{9} = 1$$

All the probabilities must equal $\frac{9}{9}$

$$\frac{5}{9} + \frac{1}{9} = \frac{6}{9}$$

$$\frac{9}{9} - \frac{6}{9} = \frac{3}{9}$$

so $\quad P(\text{yellow}) = \frac{3}{9}$

4.4 The probability that something will not happen

In the previous example, the probability of getting a yellow cube was $\frac{3}{9}$.

The probability of choosing a colour other than yellow was $\frac{6}{9}$.

This is because $1 - \frac{3}{9} = \frac{6}{9}$.

■ **If the probability of an event happening is P, then the probability of it not happening is $1 - $ P.**

Example 5

The probability of winning a prize in the school raffle is $\frac{1}{200}$.
What is the probability of not winning a prize?

$$P(\text{not winning}) = 1 - P(\text{winning})$$
$$= 1 - \frac{1}{200}$$
$$= \frac{199}{200}$$

Exercise 4C

1 A biased die is thrown. The probability that it will give an odd number is $\frac{2}{6}$.
   The probability that it will give 6 is $\frac{2}{6}$.
   What is the probability that it will give an even number that is not 6?

A biased die is *unfair* because it is weighted so that it is more likely to land on some numbers rather than others.

2 Terry wants a hot drink.
   He chooses between coffee, tea and hot chocolate.
   There is a probability of $\frac{3}{17}$ that he will choose tea and $\frac{7}{17}$ that he will choose coffee.
   What is the probability that he will choose hot chocolate?

3 Joan does not like coffee so she chooses a hot drink from tea or hot chocolate. There is a probability of $\frac{3}{5}$ that she chooses tea.
   (a) What is the probability that she will choose coffee?
   (b) What is the probability that she will choose hot chocolate?

4 If I roll an ordinary die what is the probability that I will get
   (a) an integer
   (b) a number less than 10
   (c) a decimal number
   (d) a prime number
   (e) a number that is not prime.

An ordinary die is *fair* because it is equally likely that you will land on any number.

5 Surmey chooses a card from an ordinary pack of playing cards.
   (a) What is the probability that it is a diamond?
   (b) What is the probability that it is not a diamond?

6 Jim owns a greyhound called Spot. He says Spot has a probability of $\frac{3}{15}$ of winning a race.
   What is the probability that Spot will not win the race?

7 There are five horses in a race with equal chances of winning. Four horses are grey and one is black.
   (a) What is the probability that the black horse will win?
   (b) What is the probability that the black horse will not win?

8 Sharon takes phone orders for bouquets of flowers. The probability of her making a mistake with the order is $\frac{2}{15}$.

What is the probability of her taking the order correctly?

4.5 Experimental probability

Sometimes we use experiments to estimate the probability of an outcome.

For example, you can estimate the probability of getting a 3 on a dice by rolling the dice several times and keeping a record of the total number of trials and the number of times the outcome was 3.

If you rolled the dice 10 times and 3 turned up 4 times, the experimental probability of rolling a 3 would be $\frac{4}{10}$ or $P(3) = \frac{4}{10}$.

When you count the number of times a certain event happens and the total number of trials you can find the experimental probability.

■ **The estimated or experimental probability that an event will happen is:**

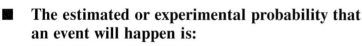

$$\frac{\textbf{the number of successful trials}}{\textbf{the total number of trials}}$$

The theoretical probability is found by saying all events are equally likely.

On a normal dice there are six possible outcomes and one of them is the number 3.

The theoretical probability of rolling a 3 would be $P(3) = \frac{1}{6}$.

■ **The theoretical probability that something will happen is:**

$$\frac{\textbf{the number of successful outcomes}}{\textbf{the total number of possible outcomes}}$$

Experimental probability is used when you do not know the total number of outcomes or whether they are equally likely. For example, with an unfair six-sided dice you can use an experiment to find the chance of each outcome happening.

Experimental probability means that you **do** an experiment to get the information to work out the chance of an outcome happening.

Theoretical probability is used when you know the total number of possible outcomes and that they are all equally likely. For example, for a fair ordinary dice there are six equally likely possible outcomes.

Theoretical probability means that you **think** about the event to get the information to work out the chance of an outcome happening.

Example 6

A sweet factory produces a variety pack of boiled sweets.
The flavours are lime, strawberry, lemon and orange.
Mary wanted to estimate the probability of picking a
particular flavour from a full pack of sweets without
looking. She picked out a sweet from a pack and replaced it
after noting its flavour. She repeated this 20 times.
Her results are shown below.

Estimate the probability of picking a lime sweet from a full
pack.

Flavour	No. of times picked
Lime	4
Lemon	6
Strawberry	7
Orange	3

There were 20 trials and there were four successful trials
for lime, so the estimated probability of choosing a lime-
flavoured sweet is $\frac{4}{20}$.

Exercise 4D

1 Make a 6-sided dice from a piece of board, sellotaping
a small counter on the inside of the side labelled 6.

   (a) Is this a fair dice?

   (b) What is the theoretical probability of throwing a 6
   when a fair dice is thrown?

   (c) Throw your dice 60 times and record in a table the
   number of times 1, 2, 3, 4, 5 and 6 occur.

   (d) Estimate the probability of getting a 6 with your dice.

2 Place 20 counters of four different colours in a bag. Do
not reveal how many counters of each colour there are.
Ask the person sitting next to you to pick out a counter,
note the colour and replace it. Repeat this 20 times.

   (a) Write the estimated probabilities of each of the
   colours being picked.

(b) Empty out your bag and calculate the probabilities of choosing each colour.

(c) Were your estimated probabilities close to the calculated probabilities?

3 Throw a 10p coin and a 2p coin at the same time. Record your result. Repeat this 30 times.

(a) Estimate the probability of getting two heads.

(b) Pool your results with the person sitting next to you. Find the new estimate for getting two heads with the 60 results.

(c) What is the theoretical probability of getting two heads (you can list all the possible outcomes to find this)?

(d) Pool the results of the whole class. What is the experimental probability now?

(e) Compare your theoretical result to your experimental results. Are they similar?

4.6 Combined events

When two events happen at the same time we can use **sample spaces** to show all the possible outcomes clearly.

For example, when two coins are thrown we can draw the following sample space diagram:

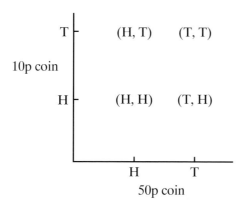

■ **When two events occur at the same time you can show all the possible outcomes on a sample space diagram.**

Example 7

A restaurant in Madrid has a menu of three starters, soup, tuna salad or garlic mushrooms, and four main courses, omelette, grilled fish, lasagne or risotto.

(a) Show all the possible outcomes for choosing a starter and a main course.

(b) A tourist does not understand the menu and chooses a starter and a main course at random. Find the probability of the tourist choosing soup and omelette.

(c) What is the probability of choosing the grilled fish with any starter?

(a)

soup	(omelette, soup)	(fish, soup)	(lasagne, soup)	(risotto, soup)
Starter salad	(omelette, salad)	(fish, salad)	(lasagne, salad)	(risotto, salad)
mushroom	(omelette, mushroom)	(fish, mushroom)	(lasagne, mushroom)	(risotto, mushroom)
	omelette	fish	lasagne	risotto

Main course

(b) There are 12 possible outcomes and only one of these is soup and omelette, so the probability of choosing this combination is $\frac{1}{12}$.

(c) There are three different starters to have with grilled fish so the probability of choosing fish and any starter is $\frac{3}{12}$.

Exercise 4E

1

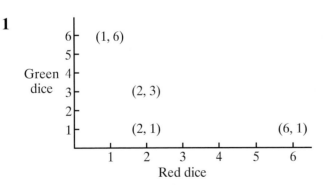

(a) This is the sample space for a pair of dice being thrown. Copy and complete the sample space.

  (b) How many possible outcomes are there when two dice are thrown together?

  (c) Calculate the probability of getting two numbers the same.

  (d) Find the probability of getting two prime numbers.

  (e) Find the probability of getting a pair of numbers that add up to less than 5.

2 Use the sample space on page 71 to find the probability of getting two tails when two coins are tossed together.

3 Caroline and Monica are playing with a coin and a 5-sided spinner.

  (a) Draw a sample space to show all the different combinations they can get.

  (b) Find the probability of getting an odd number and a head.

Summary of key points

1 Probability uses numbers to measure the chance of an outcome happening.

2 An outcome that is certain to happen has a probability of 1.

3 An outcome that cannot happen has a probability of 0.

4 All probabilities have a value from 0 to 1.

5 The probability that something will happen is

$$P(\text{event}) = \frac{\text{the number of successful outcomes}}{\text{the total number of possible outcomes}}$$

6 The probabilities of all the possible outcomes of an event add up to 1.

7 If the probability of an event happening is P, then the probability of it not happening is $1 - P$.

8 The estimated or experimental probability that an event will happen is:

$$\frac{\text{the number of successful trials}}{\text{the total number of trials}}$$

9 The theoretical probability that something will happen is:

$$\frac{\text{the number of successful outcomes}}{\text{the total number of possible outcomes}}$$

10 When two events occur at the same time you can show all the possible outcomes on a sample space diagram.

5 Working with decimals

5.1 Adding and subtracting decimal numbers

It is useful to be able to add and subtract decimals quickly in your head.

Example 1

Fill in the number that should go in the box to make these true:

(a) $0.7 + \boxed{} = 1$

(b) $0.28 + \boxed{} = 1$

(c) $6 - 0.1 = \boxed{}$

(d) $1 - \boxed{} = 0.42$

To answer this question in your head you need to be able to work out parts of numbers that add together to give 1.

eg
$$0.4 + 0.6 = 1$$
$$0.8 + 0.2 = 1$$
$$0.45 + 0.55 = 1$$
$$0.21 + 0.79 = 1$$

(a) $0.7 + \boxed{0.3} = 1$

(b) $0.28 + \boxed{0.72} = 1$

(c) $6 - 0.1 = \boxed{5.9}$

(d) $1 - \boxed{0.58} = 0.42$

Example 2

Calculate $21.62 - 5.9$

$$21.62 - 5.9 = 21.62 - 5 - 0.9 = 21.62 - 5 - 0.62 - 0.28$$
$$= 16.62 - 0.62 - 0.28$$
$$= 16 - 0.28$$
$$= 15.72$$

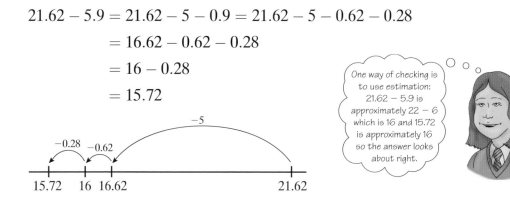

One way of checking is to use estimation: $21.62 - 5.9$ is approximately $22 - 6$ which is 16 and 15.72 is approximately 16 so the answer looks about right.

Exercise 5A

1 This diagram shows pairs of decimal numbers that add up to 1.

Copy and complete the diagram by filling in the missing answers:

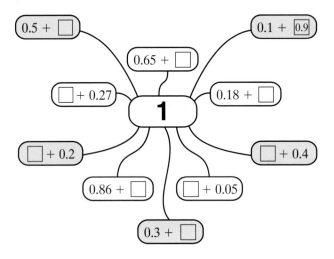

2 Without doing any working on paper, write down the numbers that should go in the boxes to make these true:

(a) $3.7 + \square = 4$ (b) $4.6 + \square = 5$

(c) $8.27 + \square = 9$ (d) $8 - 2.4 = \square$

(e) $5 - 3.8 = \square$ (f) $4.71 + \square = 8$

(g) $7 - 4.36 = \square$ (h) $12.25 + \square = 15$

(i) $8 - \square = 4.52$

3 (a) If $12.2 - 0.5 = 11.7$ what is $11.7 + 0.5$?

(b) If $9.6 + 4.5 = 14.1$ what is $14.1 - 9.6$?

(c) If $4.7 - 3.2 = 1.5$ what is $4.7 - 1.5$?

4 Work these out mentally and write the answer

(a) $5.6 + 2.9$ [Hint: it's easier to add 3 first and then take off 0.1]

(b) $2.5 + 2.7$ [Hint: this is a 'near-double']

(c) $8.2 + 2.2$ [Hint: add the whole numbers and decimals separately]

It is also important to be able to add and subtract decimal numbers using written methods.

Example 3

Andrew buys 1.2 kg of potatoes, a bag of peanuts weighing 60 g and a loaf of bread weighing 0.84 kg. Calculate the total weight of Andrew's shopping in kg.

First make sure all units are the same.

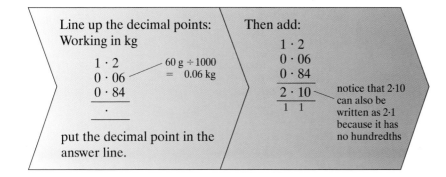

The total weight is 2.1 kg.

Example 4

Calculate $85.86 - 24.347$ showing all your working.

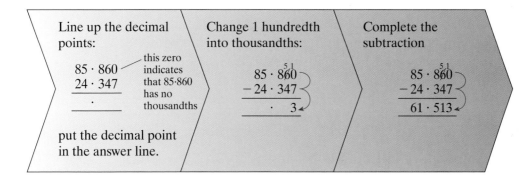

■ **To add or subtract decimals:**
   - **line up the decimal points**
   - **put the point in the answer**
   - **add or subtract**

Exercise 5B

Show all your working.

1. **(a)** £46.78 + £27.45   **(b)** £5.48 + £26.72
   (c) 2.85 kg + 3.95 kg   **(d)** 7.59 m + 8.73 m

2. **(a)** 5.6 + 2.9   **(b)** 8.2 + 1.95
   (c) 128.7 + 0.53   **(d)** 9.02 + 0.793

3. **(a)** 68.9 + 5.85 + 0.06   **(b)** 7.9 + 6.3 + 5.82
   (c) 12 + 26.9 + 7.25   **(d)** 7.48 + 15 + 0.862

4. **(a)** £5.94 − £2.36   **(b)** £13.40 − £9.87
   (c) 18.23 kg − 4.65 kg   **(d)** 7.85 m − 2.48 m

5. **(a)** 7.4 − 3.8   **(b)** 2.45 − 0.97
   (c) 2.3 − 1.8   **(d)** 13.218 − 5.635

6. **(a)** 240.3 − 3.7   **(b)** 2.08 − 0.63
   (c) 12.4 − 8.93   **(d)** 5 − 2.76

7. Bhavana put 0.9 kg of water and 350 g of rice into an empty saucepan weighing 1.16 kg. Work out the total weight of the saucepan and its contents.

8. Mark's empty bag weighs 1.8 kg. One day he had in his bag a book, weighing 1.7 kg, three exercise books weighing 0.28 kg each, a pencil case weighing 0.24 kg and a calculator weighing 0.17 kg. What was the total weight of Mark's bag and its contents?

9. The temperature in Luton at noon was 16.2°C. By midnight the temperature had fallen by 7.5°C. What was the temperature in Luton at midnight?

10. Linda cut lengths of 0.68 m and 1.24 m from a four metre piece of ribbon. Work out the length of ribbon left over.

5.2 **Writing decimal numbers in size order**

To arrange decimal numbers in order of size you need to have a good understanding of place value.

■ **You can sort decimal numbers in order of size by first comparing the whole numbers, then the digits in the tenths place, then the digits in the hundredths place, and so on.**

Example 5

Write these decimal numbers in order of size, starting with the largest: 3.069,   5.2,   3.4,   3.08,   7.0

Step 1:	**Step 2:**	**Step 3:**
Whole numbers:	Tenths place:	Hundredths place:
7 is bigger than 5	**4** is bigger than **0**	8 is bigger than 6
5 is bigger than 3		
7.0	7.0	7.0
5.2	5.2	5.2
3.069	3.4	3.4
3.4		
3.08	3.069	3.08
	3.08	3.069

So the order is   7,   5.2,   3.4,   3.08,   3.069.

Exercise 5C

1 Rearrange these decimal numbers in order of size, starting with the largest:

   (a) 0.62, 0.71, 0.68, 0.76, 0.9   **(b)** 3.4, 3.12, 3.75, 2.13, 2.09

   (c) 5.2, 3.6, 5.04, 5.16, 3.47   **(d)** 0.42, 0.065, 0.407, 0.3, 0.09

   (e) 3.0, 6.52, 6.08, 3.58, 3.7   **(f)** 0.06, 0.13, 0.009, 0.105, 0.024

   (g) 0.08, 0.8, 0.05, 0.2, 0.525   **(h)** 2.09, 1.08, 2.2, 1.3, 1.16

2 Put these decimal numbers in order of size, smallest first:

   (a) 4.85, 5.9, 5.16, 4.09, 5.23   **(b)** 0.34, 0.09, 0.37, 0.021, 0.4

   (c) 5, 7.23, 5.01, 7.07, 5.009   **(d)** 1.001, 0.23, 1.08, 1.14, 0.07

5.3 Multiplying decimals

You can multiply decimal numbers by 10, 100 and 1000 by using the idea of place value.

■ **To multiply decimals**
- **by 10 move the digits one place to the left.**
- **by 100 move the digits two places to the left.**
- **by 1000 move the digits three places to the left.**

Th	H	T	U.	t	h	th
		5	6.	2	1	
		5	7.	3	8	4
			0.	9	3	

× 10 =
× 100 =
× 1000 =

Th	H	T	U.	t	h	th
	5	6	2.	1		
5	7	3	8.	4		
		9	3.	0		

Example 6

Without using a calculator write down the answers to:

(a) 3.68×10 **(b)** 0.17×1000

(a) $3.68 \times 10 = 36.8$ Move the digits 1 place to the left

(b) $0.17 \times 1000 = 170$ Move the digits 3 places to the left.

To multiply decimals by small whole numbers you can use 'short multiplication'.

Example 7

Find the cost of 6 books at £5.28 each.

First multiply the numbers together ignoring the decimal point:

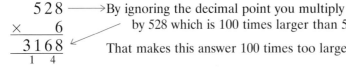

```
   5 2 8  ──→ By ignoring the decimal point you multiply
 ×     6          by 528 which is 100 times larger than 5.28
 ─────────
   3 1 6 8  ←──  That makes this answer 100 times too large.
   1   4
```

To find the final answer, divide by 100:

Th	H	T	U.	t	h	th
3	1	6	8.			

÷ 100 =

Th	H	T	U.	t	h	th
		3	1.	6	8	

So the cost of the books is £31.68.

Notice that 5.28 and 31.68 both have 2 decimal places.

Easy Maths Price £5.28

■ **When multiplying a decimal number by a whole number, the answer has the same number of digits after the decimal point as the decimal number being multiplied.**

To multiply decimal numbers by larger whole numbers you can use a long multiplication method.

Example 8

Work out 6.72×34

$6.72 \times 34 = 6.72 \times 4 + 6.72 \times 30$

$$6.72 \times 4 = \underset{2}{26.88}$$

$6.72 \times 30 = 6.72 \times 10 \times 3 = 67.2 \times 3 = \underset{2}{201.6}$

Adding, $\qquad 6.72 \times 34 = \underset{1}{228.48}$

So $6.72 \times 34 = 228.48$

6.72×34 is approximately $7 \times 30 = 210$ so this answer looks about right

To multiply a decimal number by another decimal number without using a calculator, you could convert the decimal numbers to fractions.

For example, to work out 0.4×0.7:

$$0.4 \times 0.7 = \frac{4}{10} \times \frac{7}{10} = \frac{4 \times 7}{10 \times 10} = \frac{28}{100} = 0.28$$

$\div 10$ **and** $\div 10$ is equivalent to $\div 100$

So $0.4 \times 0.7 = 0.28$

In the same way, to work out 8.2×4.3

$$8.2 \times 4.3 = \frac{82}{10} \times \frac{43}{10}$$

$$= \frac{82 \times 43}{10 \times 10}$$

$$= \frac{3526}{100}$$

$$= 35.26$$

Work out 82×43
by long multiplication

$$
\begin{array}{r}
82 \\
\times \ \ 43 \\
\hline
246 \\
3280 \\
\hline
3526 \\
\end{array}
$$

■ **If you multiply a number with one decimal place by another number with one decimal place, the answer will have two decimal places**

e.g. $8.2 \times 4.3 = 35.26$

Example 9

Work out 5.4×3.7

5.4×3.7 is approximately $5 \times 4 = 20$
By long multiplication $54 \times 37 = 1998$

The answer will have two digits to the right of the decimal point

so $5.4 \times 3.7 = 19.98$

Work out 54×37
by long multiplication

$$
\begin{array}{r}
54 \\
\times\ \ 37 \\
\hline
37\overset{2}{8} \\
16\overset{1}{2}0 \\
\hline
1998 \\
\end{array}
$$

Exercise 5D

Write down the answers in questions **1** and **2**.

1 (a) 3.29×100 (b) 46.2×10
   (c) 0.213×10 (d) 0.063×10
   (e) 9.24×1000 (f) 0.07×100

2 (a) 7.93×100 (b) 53.62×10
   (c) 4.123×1000 (d) 5.21×10
   (e) 38.5×100 (f) 0.06×1000

3 Find the cost of

   (a) 5 books at £4.37 each.
   (b) 4 kg of apples at £0.64 per kg.
   (c) 8 chocolate bars at £0.45 each.
   (d) 6 packets of crisps at £1.38 each.

Work out the answers to questions **4** and **5**, showing all your working.

4 (a) 7.8×2 (b) 5.6×4 (c) 8.4×5
   (d) 2.35×3 (e) 14.6×8 (f) 5.29×6

5 (a) 53.67×9 (b) 7.6×5 (c) 28.63×7
   (d) 8.76×5 (e) 9.25×4 (f) 15.99×8

6 Work out the cost of 9 CDs which cost £12.99 each.

7 Find the total length, in metres, of seven pieces of wood, each 0.65 metre long.

8 Work out the total length, in metres, of six pieces of wire, each 0.34 metre long.

9 Find the total cost, in pounds (£), of three loaves at £0.82 each and eight cakes at £0.55 each.

10 Calculate the total cost of five cartons of fruit juice which cost £0.70 each and seven packets of biscuits which cost £0.56 each.

11 Work out:

    (a) 6.24×23 **(b)** 5.31×42 **(c)** 4.62×37

    (d) 23.42×43 **(e)** 52.62×35 **(f)** 89.57×76

12 Find the answers:

    (a) 0.3×0.6 **(b)** 0.7×0.8 **(c)** 1.4×0.6

    (d) 2.3×4.1 **(e)** 5.4×1.9 **(f)** 5.8×7.6

5.4 Dividing decimals

Dividing decimals by 10, 100 and 1000 also involves using the idea of place value.

■ **To divide decimals**
 - **by 10 move the digits one place to the right.**
 - **by 100 move the digits two places to the right.**
 - **by 1000 move the digits three places to the right.**

Th	H	T	U	t	h	th
		6	5 .	7	4	
		3	6 .	5		
	8	9	1 .			

÷ 10 =
÷ 100 =
÷ 1000 =

Th	H	T	U	t	h	th
			6 .	5	7	4
			0 .	3	6	5
			0 .	8	9	1

Example 10

Without using a calculator write down the answers to:

(a) $53.19 \div 100$ **(b)** $6.4 \div 1000$

(a) $53.19 \div 100 = 0.5319$ Move the digits 2 places to the right.

(b) $6.4 \div 1000 = 0.0064$ Move the digits 3 places to the right.
To do this you need to put in two zeros.

You can also divide decimal numbers by whole numbers by using short division.

Example 11

Four friends had a meal in a café and they decided to pay equal amounts towards the cost. The total bill came to £18.32. How much should they each pay?

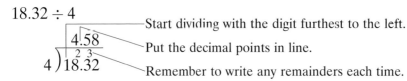

$18.32 \div 4$

Start dividing with the digit furthest to the left.

Put the decimal points in line.

Remember to write any remainders each time.

$$4.58$$
$$4\,)\,18.^{2}3^{3}2$$

You could work in pence. The answer would be 458p = £4.58

They should each pay £4.58.

- ■ **When dividing a decimal by a whole number put the decimal point in the answer above the decimal point in the number being divided.**

Example 12

Calculate $0.28 \div 8$

2 divided by 8 gives 0 remainder 2.

$$0.0\;3\;5$$
$$8\,)\,0.2^{2}8^{4}0$$

The remainder is carried over to the 8 to give 28 hundredths.
Then 28 hundredths is divided by 8 to give 3 hundredths and remainder 4.
The 4 is carried over to the zero to give 40 thousandths.
40 thousandths divided by 8 gives 5 thousandths

The answer is 0.035.

Example 13

Work out $66.15 \div 0.7$

$66.15 \div 0.7$ is approximately $70 \div 1 = 70$
You need to change 0.7 to a whole number by multiplying by 10.

$$66.15 \div 0.7 = \frac{66.15}{0.7} \overset{\times 10}{\underset{\times 10}{=}} \frac{661.5}{7}$$

$$7 \overline{) 66^{3}1.^{3}5} \overset{94.5}{}$$

So $66.15 \div 0.7 = 94.5$

Exercise 5E

Write down the answers for question **1**.

1 **(a)** $382 \div 10$ **(b)** $29.3 \div 100$
   (c) $4286.1 \div 10$ **(d)** $532.8 \div 1000$
   (e) $3.7 \div 100$ **(f)** $28.5 \div 1000$
   (g) $0.06 \div 10$ **(h)** $3.8 \div 1000$

2 Find one share if

   (a) Four people share £5.08 equally,
   (b) Seven people share £215.60 equally,
   (c) Six people share £10.50 equally,
   (d) Eight people share £30.24 equally.

3 Write down the answers for these questions showing all your working:

   (a) $8.6 \div 2$ **(b)** $5.6 \div 4$ **(c)** $120.5 \div 5$
   (d) $187.2 \div 3$ **(e)** $38.82 \div 6$ **(f)** $17.28 \div 8$
   (g) $0.612 \div 6$ **(h)** $0.245 \div 7$ **(i)** $1.08 \div 4$
   (j) $0.0057 \div 3$ **(k)** $9.054 \div 9$ **(l)** $3.75 \div 5$

4 10.8 litres of lemonade is poured into six jugs, with the same amount in each jug. How much lemonade is in each jug?

5 Four people share equally the cost of hiring a taxi. The taxi costs £28.60. How much does each person pay?

6 A load of apples weighing 67.5g is packed into 9 trays containing equal weights of apples. Work out the weight of apples in each tray.

7 Work out:

(a) $7.62 \div 0.3$ (b) $47.25 \div 0.5$

(c) $4.44 \div 0.6$ (d) $4.077 \div 0.9$

(e) $2.072 \div 0.07$ (f) $3.454 \div 0.04$

5.5 Multiplying and dividing decimal numbers mentally

You can multiply and divide some decimals mentally by small whole numbers by calculating with the whole number and decimal parts separately.

Example 14

Work these out mentally:

(a) 12.4×3 (b) $63.7 \div 7$

(a) $12.4 \times 3 = (12 \times 3) + (0.4 \times 3)$
$$= 36 + 1.2$$
$$= 37.2$$

> 12.4×3 is approximately 12×3 which is 36 so the answer looks about right

(b) $63.7 \div 7 = (63 \div 7) + (0.7 \div 7)$
$$= 9 + 0.1$$
$$= 9.1$$

> $7 \times 9 = 63$ so the answer must be a bit more than 9

You can also multiply and divide decimals mentally by larger whole numbers by using factor pairs.

There is more about factor pairs on page 3.

Example 15

Use factor pairs of the whole numbers to work out:

(a) 4.1×18 **(b)** $0.84 \div 42$

(a) $4.1 \times 18 = 4.1 \times 6 \times 3$

$18 = 6 \times 3$

so $(4.1 \times 6) = 24.6$

and $24.6 \times 3 = (24 \times 3) + (0.6 \times 3)$

$= 72 + 1.8$

$= 73.8$

> The answer should be...
> $4.1 \times 18 \approx 4 \times 20$
> ≈ 80
> ... approximately 80

(b) $0.84 \div 42 = (0.84 \div 7) \div 6$

$42 = 7 \times 6$

$0.84 \div 7 = 0.12$

$0.12 \div 6 = 0.02$

Exercise 5F

1 Work these out mentally:

(a) 3.4×2 **(b)** 5.3×3

(c) 12.2×4 **(d)** 14.3×5

(e) $12.8 \div 4$ **(f)** $129.6 \div 3$

(g) $63.9 \div 9$ **(h)** $30.4 \div 8$

2 Use factor pairs of the whole number to work out:

(a) 3.7×15 **(b)** 4.5×18

(c) 6.4×14 **(d)** $75.6 \div 18$

(e) $76.02 \div 21$ **(f)** $24.5 \div 49$

5.6 Changing decimal numbers to fractions and fractions to decimals

■ **You can write decimal numbers as fractions using the idea of place value diagrams.**

Example 16

Change 0.075 into a fraction in its simplest form.

The diagram shows that 0.075 is 7 hundredths and five thousandths, which is the same as 75 thousandths.

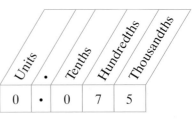

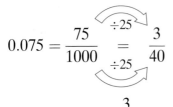

$$0.075 = \frac{75}{1000} \begin{array}{c} \div 25 \\ = \\ \div 25 \end{array} \frac{3}{40}$$

So 0.075 is equal to $\frac{3}{40}$.

$\frac{7}{100} + \frac{5}{1000} = \frac{70}{1000} + \frac{5}{1000} = \frac{75}{1000}$

Divide top and bottom by the common factor 25.

■ **To change fractions into decimal numbers divide the numerator by the denominator.**

Example 17

Change these fractions into decimal numbers:

(a) $\frac{3}{5}$ **(b)** $\frac{7}{8}$ **(c)** $\frac{68}{125}$

(a) $\frac{3}{5}$ means $3 \div 5$, which equals 0.6.

(b) $\frac{7}{8}$ means $7 \div 8$, which equals 0.875.

(c) $\frac{68}{125}$ means $68 \div 125$, which equals 0.544.

Exercise 5G

Change these decimals into fractions in their simplest form:

1 0.9	**2** 0.6	**3** 0.15	**4** 0.16
5 0.05	**6** 0.08	**7** 0.19	**8** 0.35
9 0.48	**10** 0.32	**11** 0.56	**12** 0.625
13 0.0625	**14** 0.128	**15** 0.512	**16** 0.375

Change these fractions into decimal numbers:

17 $\frac{9}{100}$ **18** $\frac{17}{100}$ **19** $\frac{23}{1000}$ **20** $\frac{2}{5}$ **21** $\frac{7}{8}$

22 $\frac{3}{4}$ **23** $\frac{4}{5}$ **24** $\frac{9}{20}$ **25** $\frac{16}{25}$ **26** $\frac{3}{40}$

27 $\frac{3}{8}$ **28** $\frac{17}{125}$ **29** $\frac{3}{16}$ **30** $\frac{13}{20}$ **31** $\frac{12}{125}$

5.7 Rounding answers to the nearest whole number

When you work out a calculation on a calculator you will sometimes be asked to round your answer to the nearest whole number.

The calculator display shows the decimal number 12.7.
The value of 12.7 is between 12 and 13.
The tenths divisions between 12 and 13 are shown on this number line:

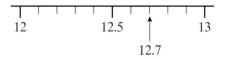

12.7 is closer to 13 than to 12 so 12.7 rounds to 13.
This is called **rounding up**.
You write "12.7 = 13 (correct to the nearest whole number)"
or "12.7 = 13 (to the nearest whole number)".

The value of 12.4 is also between 12 and 13.

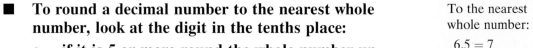

12.4 is closer to 12 than to 13 so 12.4 rounds to 12.
This is called **rounding down**.
So 12.4 = 12 (to the nearest whole number).

12.5 is halfway between 12 and 13. It is rounded up so that 12.5 = 13 (to the nearest whole number).

■ **To round a decimal number to the nearest whole number, look at the digit in the tenths place:**
  - **if it is 5 or more round the whole number up.**
  - **if it is less than 5 don't change the whole number.**

To the nearest whole number:

6.5 = 7
19.8 = 20
48.3 = 48

Example 18

Round these decimals to the nearest whole number.

(a) 57.4   (b) 29.73   (c) 36.5

(a) 57.4   The digit in the tenths place is 4, which is smaller than 5, so you do not change the whole number (you round down).

So 57.4 = 57 (to the nearest whole number).

(b) 29.73   The digit in the tenths place is 7, which is bigger than 5, so you round up and increase the whole number by 1.

So 29.73 = 30 (to the nearest whole number).

(c) 36.5   The digit in the tenths place is 5, so you round up and increase the whole number by 1.

So 36.5 = 37 (to the nearest whole number).

Rounding money answers to the nearest penny

It is often necessary to round money answers to the nearest penny.

Example 19

The total cost of hiring a coach for a visit to an exhibition is £140. The 34 passengers share the cost equally. How much does each passenger pay? Give your answer to the nearest penny.

£140 ÷ 34

Using an 8 digit calculator, the result on the calculator display is 4.1176471.

£0.1176471 is 11.76471 pence.

11.76471 rounds up to 12 pence.

Tenths place: 7 is bigger than 5, so you round up.

Each passenger pays £4.12 (to the nearest penny).

Instead, you could look at the digit in the thousandths place.

£4.1176471.

Thousandths place: 7 is bigger than 5, so you round up.

The answer is £4.12 (to the nearest penny).

■ **To round an answer in pounds to the nearest penny, look at the digit in the thousandths place:**
- **if it is 5 or more round up the whole number of pence.**
- **if it is less than 5 don't change the whole number of pence.**

To the nearest penny:
£58.237 = £58.24
£2.48513 = £2.49
£3.2638 = £3.26

Example 20

The answer to a calculation is £265.39621.
Write this answer to the nearest penny.

265.39621

Thousandths place: 6 is bigger than 5, so you
round up the whole number of pence.
The answer is £265.40 (to the nearest penny).

Exercise 5H

In questions **1** to **6** round the decimals to the nearest whole
number.

1 **(a)** 3.9 **(b)** 2.4 **(c)** 8.5 **(d)** 5.62

2 **(a)** 15.261 **(b)** 4.801 **(c)** 10.59 **(d)** 19.7

3 **(a)** 0.8 **(b)** 10.399 **(c)** 28.25 **(d)** 100.08

4 **(a)** 29.82 **(b)** 1.99 **(c)** 326.48 **(d)** 69.09

5 **(a)** 6.298 **(b)** 399.6 **(c)** 25999.7 **(d)** 28.199

6 **(a)** 79.64 **(b)** 0.75 **(c)** 39.29 **(d)** 6999.53

Questions **7** to **10** are the answers to calculations. Write the
answers to the nearest penny.

7 **(a)** £4.267 **(b)** £3.582 **(c)** £15.625

8 **(a)** £6.8425 **(b)** £0.8367 **(c)** £42.8352

9 **(a)** £178.629 43 **(b)** £5238.9421 **(c)** £24.638 915

10 **(a)** £178.298 45 **(b)** £1638.9218 **(c)** £213.8954

In questions **11** to **13** give your answers to the nearest penny.

11 Sophie buys a camera. The cash price of the
camera is £158. Sophie pays a deposit of one third
of the cash price. How much is the deposit?

12 Mrs Kaur gives £125 to her six grandchildren in
equal shares. How much does each grandchild
receive?

13 The price of a Hi-Fi is £248.99. Harry pays for the
Hi-Fi in five equal instalments. Work out the amount
of one instalment.

5.8 Rounding to a number of decimal places

The last section showed how amounts of money in pounds can be rounded to the nearest penny. This is the same as rounding to 2 decimal places.

■ **You can round decimal numbers to a given number of decimal places (dp).**
The first decimal place is the first position after the decimal point.

Example 21

Write 24.683 correct to 2 decimal places.

Look at the digit in the third decimal place:

24.68**3**

Tens	Units	.	First decimal place (1dp)	Second decimal place (2dp)	Third decimal place (3dp)
2	4	.	6	8	3

The digit is 3 which is smaller than 5, so you do not need to change the digit in the second decimal place.

24.68$|$3
= 24.68 (to 2 dp)

So 24.683 = 24.68 (correct to 2 decimal places).

You can write this as 24.68 (to 2 dp).

Example 22

Round 5.2397   **(a)** to 1 dp   **(b)** to 2 dp   **(c)** to 3 dp

(a) Look at the next digit after the 1st decimal place.
It is 3, so you do not round up.
5.2397 = 5.2 (to 1 dp)

5.2$|$397

(b) Look at the next digit after the 2nd decimal place.
It is 9, so you round up.
5.2397 = 5.24 (to 2 dp)

5.23$|$97

(c) Look at the next digit after the 3rd decimal place.
It is 7, so you round up.
5.2397 = 5.240 (to 3 dp)

5.239$|$7

You must include the final zero, as '**3 dp**' means that **three** decimal places must be shown

Recurring decimals

$0.7777777\ldots$ is called **0.7 recurring**. It is written $0.\dot{7}$ (with a dot over the 7) for short.

Example 23

Change these fractions to decimals, giving your answers to 3 decimal places.

(a) $\frac{1}{3}$ (b) $\frac{2}{3}$ (c) $\frac{3}{7}$

(a) $\frac{1}{3}$ means $1 \div 3$, which equals $0.33333\ldots$ (or $0.\dot{3}$) $0.333\vert33\ldots$

     So $\frac{1}{3} = 0.333$ (to 3 dp).

(b) $\frac{2}{3}$ means $2 \div 3$, which equals $0.66666\ldots$ (or $0.\dot{6}$) $0.666\vert66\ldots$

     So $\frac{2}{3} = 0.667$ (to 3 dp).

(c) $\frac{3}{7}$ means $3 \div 7$, which equals $0.42857\ldots$ $0.428\vert57$

     So $\frac{3}{7} = 0.429$ (to 3 dp).

Exercise 5I

1. Round each number to 1 dp.
   (a) 12.78   (b) 24.83   (c) 5.261   (d) 0.835

2. Round each number to 2 dp.
   (a) 4.239   (b) 12.222   (c) 8.165   (d) 0.0428

3. Round each number to 3 dp.
   (a) 5.8623   (b) 1.0007   (c) 5.3284   (d) 0.0498

4. Round each number to 4 dp.
   (a) 1.56325   (b) 0.02384   (c) 0.00003   (d) 8.59996

5. Change these fractions to decimals, giving your answers correct to 3 decimal places..
   (a) $\frac{1}{6}$ (b) $\frac{2}{9}$ (c) $\frac{6}{7}$ (d) $\frac{4}{15}$
   (e) $\frac{19}{24}$ (f) $\frac{5}{6}$ (g) $\frac{5}{18}$ (h) $\frac{3}{11}$

5.9 Estimating answers using approximations

A way of checking your answer to a calculation is to make an estimate.

■ **To estimate an answer to a calculation:**
  ● **round all the numbers to one significant figure (1 sf).**
  ● **do the calculation with the rounded numbers.**

Example 24

Estimate the answer to:

(a) £11.20 × 6.1   (b) £19.38 ÷ 2.9   (c) $\dfrac{29.75 + 10.318}{0.45 \times 4.2}$

(a) Rounding 11.20 and 6.1 to 1 sf gives 10 and 6.
  So the estimate for £11.20 × 6.1 is £10 × 6 = £60.   Actual answer: £68.32

(b) Rounding 19.38 and 2.9 to 1 sf gives 20 and 3.
  So the estimate for £19.38 ÷ 2.9 is £20 ÷ 3 = £6$\frac{2}{3}$.   Actual answer: £6.68

(c) An estimate is $\dfrac{30 + 10}{0.5 \times 4} = \dfrac{40}{2} = 20$ Actual answer: 21.2

Multiplying and dividing by numbers between nought and one

If you multiply 6 by 0.3 the result is 1.8, which is smaller than 6.
If you multiply 58 by 0.72 the result is 41.76, which is smaller than 58.

■ **If you start with any number and multiply by a decimal number between 0 and 1, the result will be smaller than the number you started with.**

If you divide 32 by 0.4 the result is 80, which is bigger than 32.
If you divide 10.95 by 0.75 the result is 14.6, which is bigger than 10.95.

■ **If you start with any number and divide it by a decimal number between 0 and 1, the result will be bigger than the number you started with.**

When estimating answers, remember to round any decimal numbers between 0 and 1 to 1 significant figure and **not** to the nearest whole number (which would be 0 or 1).

Example 25

In part **(a)** and part **(b)**

(i)   Work out an estimate for the answer.
(ii) Use a calculator to work out the exact value.
(iii) State whether the estimate is a reasonable
      approximation for the exact value.

(a) 21.35×0.86 **(b)** $8.865 \div 0.18$

(a) **(i)**   Rounding 21.35 and 0.86 to 1 sf gives 20 and 0.9, so
         an estimate for 21.35×0.86 is

$$20 \times 0.9 = \tfrac{20}{1} \times \tfrac{9}{10} = \tfrac{180}{10} = 18$$

   (ii) Using a calculator, $21.35 \times 0.86 = 18.361$.
   (iii) Yes, 18 is a reasonable approximation for 18.361.

(b) **(i)**   Rounding 8.865 and 0.18 to 1 sf gives 9 and 0.2, so
         an estimate for $8.865 \div 0.18$ is

$$9 \div 0.2 = 9 \div \tfrac{2}{10} = \tfrac{9}{1} \times \tfrac{10}{2} = \tfrac{90}{2} = 45$$

   (ii) $8.865 \div 0.18 = 49.25$.
   (iii) Yes, 45 is a reasonable approximation for 49.25.

Exercise 5J

In each question
(i)   using approximate values, write down a calculation that
      could be used to estimate the answer,
(ii) use your values to work out the estimated answer,
      without a calculator,
(iii) use a calculator to work out the exact answer.

1 £12.35 × 4.8	**2** £39.20 × 2.1	**3** £1907.45 × 5.2
4 £7.79 ÷ 4.1	**5** £28.71 ÷ 2.9	**6** £57.97 ÷ 2.2
7 £302.15 × 4.2	**8** £37.886 ÷ 3.8	**9** £31.92 ÷ 1.9
10 4.15 × 0.92	**11** 5.9 × 0.28	**12** 4.187 ÷ 0.79

13 $\dfrac{19.2 + 31.5}{5}$ **14** $\dfrac{81.13 - 19.6}{4.2}$ **15** $2.9 \times (21.4 + 39.27)$

16 $\dfrac{59.2 - 20.44}{3.2 + 4.96}$ **17** $\dfrac{39.3 + 21.12}{0.53 \times 4}$ **18** $\dfrac{91.4 - 5.21}{0.425 \times 5.2}$

Summary of key points

1 To add or subtract decimals:
   - line up the decimal points
   - put the point in the answer
   - add or subtract.

2 You can sort decimal numbers in order of size by first comparing the whole numbers, then the digits in the tenths place, then the digits in the hundredths place, and so on.

3 To multiply decimals
   - by 10 move the digits one place to the left.
   - by 100 move the digits two places to the left.
   - by 1000 move the digits three places to the left.

4 When multiplying a decimal number by a whole number, the answer has the same number of digits after the decimal point as the decimal number being multiplied.

5 If you multiply a number with one decimal place by another number with one decimal place, the answer will have two decimal places.
   e.g. $8.2 \times 4.3 = 35.26$

6 To divide decimals
   - by 10 move the digits one place to the right.
   - by 100 move the digits two places to the right.
   - by 1000 move the digits three places to the right.

7 When dividing a decimal by a whole number put the decimal point in the answer above the decimal point in the number being divided.

8 You can write decimal numbers as fractions using the idea of place value diagrams.

9 To change fractions into decimal numbers divide the numerator by the denominator.

10 To round a decimal number to the nearest whole number, look at the digits in the tenths place:
  - if it is 5 or more round the whole number up.
  - if it is less than 5 don't change the whole number.

11 To round an answer in pounds to the nearest penny, look at the digit in the thousandths place:
  - if it is 5 or more round up the whole number of pence.
  - if it is less than 5 don't change the whole number of pence.

12 You can round decimal numbers to a given number of decimal places (dp).
  The first decimal place is the first position after the decimal point.

13 To estimate an answer to a calculation:
  - round all the numbers to one significant figure (1 sf).
  - do the calculation with the rounded numbers.

14 If you start with any number and multiply by a decimal number between 0 and 1, the result will be smaller than the number you started with.

15 If you start with any number and divide it by a decimal number between 0 and 1, the result will be bigger than the number you started with.

6 Percentages

6.1 Percentages as fractions and decimals

You can describe parts of a whole object using percentages
as well as fractions and decimals.
The symbol % means 'per cent' or 'in every hundred'.
So 19 per cent (written 19% for short) means '19 in every
hundred'. This can be written as the fraction $\frac{19}{100}$.

You can also say
'19 out of a hundred'

■ **A percentage can be written as a fraction with the
denominator 100.**

Example 1

Write $33\frac{1}{3}\%$ as a fraction in its simplest form.

Do this in two steps:

$$33\frac{1}{3}\% = \frac{33\frac{1}{3}}{100} \overset{\times 3}{\underset{\times 3}{=}} \frac{100}{300} \overset{\div 100}{\underset{\div 100}{=}} \frac{1}{3}$$

Multiply top and
bottom by 3 to
get a whole
number on top.

Divide top and
bottom by the
common factor
100.

$\dfrac{33\frac{1}{3}}{100}$

In this fraction
the denominator
is 3, so you
multiply top and
bottom by 3.

So $33\frac{1}{3}\%$ is equal to $\frac{1}{3}$.

You can also change percentages to decimals.

$$8\% = \tfrac{8}{100} = 8 \div 100 = 0.08$$

Remember: to divide
by 100 move the digits
two places to the right.
31% = 0.31

■ **To change a percentage to a decimal divide by 100.**

Example 2

Change to decimals: **(a)** 3% **(b)** 17.5%

(a) $3\% = \dfrac{3}{100} = 3 \div 100 = 0.03$ **(b)** $17.5\% = \dfrac{17.5}{100} = 17.5 \div 100 = 0.175$

■ **To change a decimal to a percentage multiply the decimal by 100%.**

■ **To change a fraction to a percentage change the fraction to a decimal and multiply the decimal by 100%.**

■ **To change a percentage to a decimal divide by 100.**

Example 3

Change to percentages:

(a) 0.49   **(b)** $\frac{3}{16}$

(a) $0.49 \times 100\% = 49\%$

(b) $\frac{3}{16} = 3 \div 16 = 0.1875$
    $0.1875 \times 100\% = 18.75\%$

Exercise 6A

1 Change these percentages to fractions.

(a) 17%	**(b)** 81%	**(c)** 9%
(d) 23%	**(e)** 3%	**(f)** 99%
(g) 51%	**(h)** 11%	

2 Change these percentages to fractions in their simplest form.

(a) 40%	**(b)** 55%	**(c)** 25%
(d) 16%	**(e)** $66\frac{2}{3}\%$	**(f)** 12.5%
(g) $16\frac{2}{3}\%$	**(h)** 0.5%	

3 Change these percentages to decimals.

(a) 2%	**(b)** 58%	**(c)** 23%
(d) 95%	**(e)** 12%	**(f)** 12.5%
(g) 2.5%	**(h)** 8.2%	

4 Change these decimals and fractions to percentages:

(a) 0.23	**(b)** 0.9	**(c)** 0.07
(d) 0.816	**(e)** $\frac{3}{10}$	**(f)** $\frac{4}{5}$
(g) $\frac{3}{25}$	**(h)** $\frac{7}{8}$	

5 Copy and complete this table of equivalent percentages, fractions and decimals.

Percentage	Fraction	Decimal
60%	$\frac{3}{5}$	0.6
31%		
	$\frac{1}{4}$	
35%		
	$\frac{1}{10}$	
		0.125
8%		
	$\frac{2}{3}$	

Here are some common percentages and their equivalent fractions and decimals. It is useful to recognise them.

$25\% = \frac{1}{4} = 0.25$ $50\% = \frac{1}{2} = 0.5$ $75\% = \frac{3}{4} = 0.75$

$10\% = \frac{1}{10} = 0.1$ $20\% = \frac{1}{5} = 0.2$ $70\% = \frac{7}{10} = 0.7$

$33\frac{1}{3}\% = \frac{1}{3} = 0.3\dot{3}$ $66\frac{2}{3}\% = \frac{2}{3} = 0.6\dot{6}$ $1\% = \frac{1}{100} = 0.01$

6.2 Working out a percentage of an amount

Sometimes you can work out percentages of an amount without using a calculator.

Example 4

Work out 21% of 65 m without using a calculator.

If
$$100\% = 65\,\text{m}$$
$\div 10$ $\qquad\qquad$ $\div 10$
$$10\% = 6.5\,\text{m}$$
$\div 10$ $\qquad\qquad$ $\div 10$
$$1\% = 0.65\,\text{m}$$

so
$$21\% = 10\% + 10\% + 1\%$$
$$= 6.5\,\text{m} + 6.5\,\text{m} + 0.65\,\text{m}$$
$$= 13.65\,\text{m}$$

21% of 65 m is 13.65 m.

Some percentages can't be written as simple fractions. You might need to use a calculator.

Example 5

Calculate 23% of 84 kg

23% of 84 = 0.23 × 84 = 19.32

so 23% of 84 kg = 19.32 kg

■ **To work out the percentage of an amount:**
  ● **write the percentage as a decimal**
  ● **multiply the decimal by the amount.**

Notice that you can work out many different percentages just by knowing one:

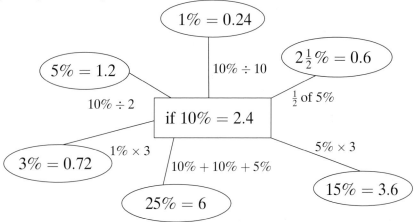

$1\% = 0.24$

$2\frac{1}{2}\% = 0.6$

$5\% = 1.2$

$10\% \div 10$

$\frac{1}{2}$ of 5%

$10\% \div 2$

if 10% = 2.4

$3\% = 0.72$

$1\% \times 3$

$10\% + 10\% + 5\%$

$5\% \times 3$

$25\% = 6$

$15\% = 3.6$

Exercise 6B

Work out the answers to questions **1**, **2**, **3** and **4** without using a calculator.

1 Of the 24 people at a bus stop, 25% have an umbrella. How many of them have an umbrella?

2 20% of the 150 pupils in Year 8 chose tennis as their favourite sport. How many of the pupils chose tennis?

3 In a sale all the marked prices were reduced by 10%. Work out the reduction for a sweater with a marked price of £23.

4 Work out

(**a**) 10% of £6   (**b**) 50% of £7   (**c**) 20% of £35

(**d**) 25% of 36 kg   (**e**) 75% of 32 m   (**f**) 30% of 40 kg

(**g**) $33\frac{1}{3}$% of 24 m   (**h**) 15% of £50   (**i**) $66\frac{2}{3}$% of 15 cm

You may use a calculator for this question.

5 Work out:

(**a**) 3% of £250   (**b**) 7% of £60   (**c**) 5% of £26

(**d**) 4% of 45 kg   (**e**) 15% of 42 m   (**f**) 17.5% of £16

(**g**) 12.5% of 20 kg   (**h**) $2\frac{1}{2}$% of 32 m   (**i**) $6\frac{1}{4}$% of £32

6.3 Increasing and decreasing by a percentage

You will often need to find the new value when an amount is increased or decreased by a percentage.

10% extra free   House prices rise by 2%   10% off all marked items

■ **To find the new value after a percentage change**
- **work out the increase and add it to the original amount, or**
- **work out the decrease and subtract it from the original amount.**

Example 6

In September the number of pupils in Year 8 at a school was 180. By the following February that number had increased by 5%. Use a non-calculator method to calculate how many pupils there were in Year 8 in February.

$$\div10 \left\{ \begin{array}{l} 100\% = 180 \\ 10\% = 18 \\ 5\% = 9 \end{array} \right\} \div10 \\ \div2$$

The increase in number of pupils = 9

The number of pupils in February = original number + increase
$$= 180 + 9 = 189$$

There were 189 pupils in Year 8 in February.

Example 7

A shop offered a discount of 15% off the usual prices. Work out the new price of a CD player originally costing £48, using a calculator.

Discount = 15% of £48   remember this means £7.20

$$= 0.15 \times 48 = 7.2$$

The new price = original price − discount

$$= £48 − £7.20$$

$$= £40.80$$

The new price of the radio is £40.80.

Exercise 6C

Do not use a calculator for questions **1** to **6**.

1 Without using a calculator, find the new amount when:

    (a) £60 is increased by 10%   **(b)** £48 is decreased by 50%

    (c) 36 m is increased by 25%   **(d)** 23 kg is decreased by 10%

    (e) 24 m is increased by 75%   **(f)** £400 is decreased by 3%

    (g) £150 is increased by 8%   **(h)** 27 kg is decreased by $33\frac{1}{3}$%

2 Last year the minimum train fare in a city was £1.20. This year all fares have increased by 5%. What is the minimum train fare now?

3 Kwong paid £275 for his clarinet four years ago. It has increased in value by 8%. Work out the value of Kwong's clarinet now.

4 Becky earns £180 a week. She is given a 3% pay rise. Work out Becky's new weekly wage. [Hint: 3% = 1% × 3].

5 On 1st May the number of pupils present at a school was 760. On 1st July, after the GCSE examinations, the number had decreased by 15%. How many pupils were present on 1st July?

6 A new car was bought for £7300. After 2 years it had lost 30% of its value. Work out the value of the car after 2 years.

You may use a calculator for the following questions.

7 In May an office had 150 employees. By September the number of employees had increased by 4%.
How many employees were there in September?

8 Last year Yasmina's Council Tax bill was £638. This year the Council Tax has risen by 3.5%.
What is Yasmina's Council Tax bill this year?

9 A travel agency offers a discount of 16% off a holiday usually costing £450. What is the new cost of the holiday?

10 In a sale prices were reduced by 20%. Work out the sale price of a coat usually priced at £42.50.

11 Find the new amount when:

    (a) £135 is increased by 7%,   **(b)** £32 is decreased by 4%,

    (c) £56 is increased by 13%,   **(d)** 62.5 kg is decreased by 8%,

    (e) 18 litres is increased by $6\frac{2}{3}$%,   **(f)** 12.8 kg is decreased by 2.5%.

6.4 Writing one quantity as a percentage of another

Sometimes you need to write one quantity as a percentage of another.

Example 8

Write 920 g as a percentage of 8 kg.

To compare the quantities the units must be the same, so change 8 kg to 8000 g.

> Hint: $g \underset{\div 1000}{\overset{\times 1000}{\rightleftarrows}} kg$
> There is more about conversion of units on page 130.

Step 1: Write as a fraction: $\frac{920}{8000}$

Step 2: Change to a decimal: $920 \div 8000 = 0.115$

Step 3: Multiply by 100%: $0.115 \times 100\% = 11.5\%$

So 920 g is 11.5% of 8 kg.

■ **To write one quantity as a percentage of another:**
  ● **write one quantity as a fraction of the other.**
  ● **change the fraction to a decimal.**
  ● **multiply the decimal by 100%.**

Remember to make sure the units are the same for both quantities.

Exercise 6D

1 There are 720 pupils in a school and 108 of them are given commendations for good work. What percentage of the pupils are given commendations?

2 Out of 80 new light bulbs tested, 78 worked. What percentage of the light bulbs worked?

3 There are 48 cars in the staff car park and 9 of them are white. What percentage of the cars are white?

4 Rowena has 150 books and 21 of them are in French. What percentage of her books are in French?

5 In a class of 32 pupils 18 are girls. What percentage of the class are **(a)** girls, **(b)** boys?

6 Of the 180 pupils in Year 8, 144 usually walk to school. Work out the percentage of year 8 pupils who usually walk to school.

7 The top mark in a test was 57 out of 60. Write this as a percentage.

8 Rob sowed 35 flower seeds and 28 of them produced plants. What percentage of the seeds produced plants?

9 750 pupils took part in a sponsored walk and 108 of them finished within 3 hours. What percentage of the pupils is this?

10 Write:
  (a) 81 pence as a percentage of £2.25
  (b) 700 m as a percentage of 2 km
  (c) 87 cm as a percentage of 3 m
  (d) 620 g as a percentage of 5 kg.

6.5 Profit and loss

If you buy an article, the price you pay is called the **cost price**. If you later sell the article, the amount of money you are paid is called the **selling price**. If you sell an item for a higher price than you paid for it you make a **profit**. If you sell it for a lower price you make a **loss**.

■ **Profit (or loss) is the difference between the cost price and the selling price.**

If a profit is made: selling price = cost price + profit

If a loss is made: selling price = cost price − loss

Example 9

Jacqui paid £5600 for a car two years ago. She recently sold the car at a loss of 23%. At what price did she sell the car?

Loss = 23% of £5600

$\quad$ = 0.23 × £5600 = £1288

Selling price = original price (or cost price) − loss

$\qquad$ = £5600 − £1288

$\qquad$ = £4312

Jacqui sold the car for £4312.

You can write the profit or loss as a percentage of the original price (the cost price).

■ **Percentage profit = $\dfrac{\text{profit}}{\text{cost price}}$ × 100%**

■ **Percentage loss = $\dfrac{\text{loss}}{\text{cost price}}$ × 100%**

Example 10

Robert bought a table for £85 in an auction and sold it in his shop for £220. Calculate the percentage profit. Give your answer to 1 decimal place.

Profit = £220 − £85 = £135.

Percentage profit = $\dfrac{\text{profit}}{\text{cost price}} \times 100\%$

$= \frac{135}{85} \times 100\%$

$= 1.5882\ldots \times 100\% = 158.82\ldots\%$

Percentage profit = 158.8% (to 1 dp)

Exercise 6E

1 For each of these calculate the selling price:
   (a) cost price = £60   profit 5%
   (b) cost price = £125 profit 6.2%
   (c) cost price = £75   loss 12%
   (b) cost price = £80   loss 23.75%

2 Zhaleh bought some jeans from a wholesaler for £21 a pair. She sells them in her shop and makes a 32% profit. What is the selling price of each pair of jeans?

3 Michael bought a radio for £62.50 and later sold it at a loss of 6.4%. At what price did Michael sell the radio?

4 For each of these calculate the percentage profit:
   (a) cost price = £80   selling price = £108
   (b) cost price = £65   selling price = £78
   (c) cost price = £120 selling price = £123

5 For each of these calculate the percentage loss:
   (a) cost price = £125 selling price = £120
   (b) cost price = £45   selling price = £40.50
   (c) cost price = £96   selling price = £84

6 Ali bought a car for £9600 and sold it for £7248. Calculate the percentage loss.

7 A shop buys a television for £525. A customer then buys the television for £700. Find the percentage profit. Give your answer to 1 decimal place.

8 Sam bought a sofa for £539, but later sold it for £480. Calculate her percentage loss, giving your answer to 1 dp.

6.6 Taxation

VAT

Value Added Tax (VAT) is the amount that is added to bills for services and purchases. In 1999 the rate for VAT in the UK was $17\frac{1}{2}\%$.

The VAT rate can be set at any percentage by the government.

Different countries have different VAT rates from each other.

Example 11

The price of a computer is £969 plus VAT at $17\frac{1}{2}\%$.

Work out the final cost, inclusive of VAT.

$$\text{VAT} = 17.5\% \text{ of } £969 = 0.175 \times 969 = 169.575$$
$$= £169.58 \text{ (to the nearest penny)}$$

Total cost = £969 + £169.58 = £1138.58.

You can use a non-calculator method to work out

Value Added Tax (VAT) at $17\frac{1}{2}\%$.

Example 12

Without using a calculator, work out the VAT at $17\frac{1}{2}\%$ on a plumber's bill of £48.

$17\frac{1}{2}\% = 17.5\% = 10\% + 5\% + 2.5\%$

10% of £48 $= \frac{1}{10} \times £48 = £48 \div 10 = £4.80$

5% is half of 10%, so 5% of £48 $\quad = £2.40$ (halving)

2.5% is half of 5%, so 2.5% of £48 $= £1.20$ (halving)

Adding, $\qquad 17.5\%$ of £48 $= £8.40$

So the VAT = £8.40

Income Tax

When you earn more than a certain amount of money you have to pay income tax to the government.

Some of your income is tax free (no income tax is paid on it) the rest of it (your **taxable income**) is taxed.

For the tax year 6th April 2000 – 5th April 2001 income tax is paid on taxable income at these rates:

Taxable income	Rate of income tax
Up to £1520	10%
£1521–£28 400	22%
Over £28 400	40%

Example 13

Calculate the tax paid by Mrs Ali. Her taxable income is £33 520.

Step 1:
Tax on the first £1520 at 10% = 10% of £1520

$$= 0.10 \times £1520$$

$$= £152$$

Step 2:
The amount of taxable income to be taxed at 22% is £28 400 − £1520 = £26 880.

Tax on the next £26 880 of taxable income at 22%

$$= 22\% \text{ of } £26\,880 = 0.22 \times 26\,880 \qquad = £5913.60$$

Step 3:
The amount of taxable income to be taxed at 40% is £33 520 − £28 400 = £5120.

Tax on the remaining £5120 of taxable income at 40%

$$= 40\% \text{ of } £5120 = 0.40 \times 5120 \qquad = £2048$$

Total tax paid = £152 + £5913.60 + £2048 = £8113.60

Exercise 6F

In this exercise take the VAT rate to be $17\frac{1}{2}\%$.

Hint:
$17\frac{1}{2}\% = 10\% + 5\% + 2\frac{1}{2}\%$

1 Without using a calculator, work out the VAT on these prices:

(a) £80   (b) £60   (c) £280   (d) £32

(e) £540   (f) £42   (g) £74   (h) £36.80

You may use a calculator for the following questions.
Give your answers to the nearest penny.

2 Work out the VAT on these prices:

(a) £18.50   (b) £56.25   (c) £210

(d) £300   (e) £682   (f) £2340

3 Add VAT to these prices:

(a) £16.52   (b) £38.24   (c) £84.99

4 Calculate the VAT on a £38.50 bill for a meal for three.

5 VAT is added to a telephone bill of £63.70.
Find the total amount to be paid.

6 An electrician charges £82.50 plus VAT for mending a washing machine. Calculate the total amount to be paid.

7

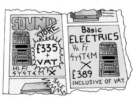

Two stores advertised the same Hi Fi system.

(a) Which is the cheaper price?
(b) What is the difference in the prices, including VAT?

8 Anna's taxable income is £14 500. Using the rates for income tax given on page 109 work out how much income tax Anna paid.

9 Using the table of tax rates on page 109 calculate the amount of income tax paid on these incomes:

(a) £3900   (b) £18 400   (c) £35 600

6.7 Buying on credit

If you want to buy items without paying the full cost
straightaway you can borrow money. This is called credit.
You may have to pay a deposit and then make a number of
regular payments to repay the loan and interest.

Example 14

The cash price of a television is £380.
Syeda bought the television on credit.
She had to pay a deposit of 15% of the
cash price and then 24 monthly payments of £17.50.

Calculate
(a) the total cost of buying the television on credit,
(b) the amount Syeda would have saved if she had paid cash.

(a) Deposit = 15% of £380 = 0.15×380 = £57
   Total monthly payments = $24 \times £17.50$ = £420
   Total credit cost = £57 + £420 = £477

(b) Difference in cost = £477 − £380 = £97
   Syeda would have saved £97 if she had paid cash.

Exercise 6G

For each question work out
(a) the total cost of buying on credit,
(b) the difference between the cash price and the cost of
   buying on credit.

1 The cash price of a gas cooker is £785. It can be
   bought with a deposit of 20% and 12 monthly
   payments of £61.70.

2 A bicycle costs £168. The credit terms are a deposit
   of 15%, followed by six monthly payments of £29.30.

3 A mini Hi Fi system costs £270. The credit
   agreement requires a deposit of 12% and
   18 monthly payments of £18.95.

4 The cash price for a conservatory is £4750. The credit terms are a deposit of 25% plus 36 monthly payments of £129.20.

5 A video recorder costs £250. It can be bought on credit with a deposit of 18% followed by 24 monthly payments of £12.65.

6 A computer costs £689. The credit terms are a deposit of 15% and 20 monthly payments of £37.50.

6.8 Simple interest

If you invest money in a bank savings account the bank pays you **interest**.

If you borrow money from a bank you pay interest to the bank. The interest is a percentage of the amount you invest or borrow.

■ **Simple interest over several years is when the sum of money invested (or borrowed) remains the same over those years and when the percentage rate of interest remains the same over those years.**

Example 15

£500 is invested for 3 years at an interest rate of 4.5% per annum. Calculate the simple interest earned.

Per annum (or p.a.) means "each year".

Interest for 1 year $= 4.5\%$ of £500 $= 0.045 \times £500 = £22.50$

Simple interest for 3 years $= £22.50 \times 3 = £67.50$.

Exercise 6H

1 Find the simple interest when
 (a) £300 is invested for 2 years at 8% p.a.
 (b) £632 is invested for 3 years at 5% p.a.
 (c) £250 is invested for 5 years at 4.6% p.a.
 (d) £728 is invested for 4 years at $5\frac{1}{2}\%$ p.a.
 (e) £360 is invested for $2\frac{1}{2}$ years at $3\frac{1}{2}\%$ p.a.

2 Rashmi invests £240 for 5 years at 6.3% per annum. Work out the simple interest he earns.

3 Sarah borrows £350 from a bank for 3 years at 8.2% per annum. Calculate

   (a) the simple interest she must pay,

   (b) the total amount she owes after 3 years.

4 Matthew wants to borrow £450 for 3 years. He can borrow from a bank at a simple interest rate of 7.2% per annum or from a credit company at a simple interest rate of 8.4% per annum. Work out the difference between the amounts of interest he would have to pay the bank and the credit company.

Summary of key points

1 A percentage can be written as a fraction with the denominator 100.

2 To change a decimal to a percentage multiply the decimal by 100%.

3 To change a fraction to a percentage change the fraction to a decimal and multiply the decimal by 100%.

4 To change a percentage to a decimal divide by 100.

5 To work out a percentage of an amount:
   • write the percentage as a decimal
   • multiply the decimal by the amount.

6 To find the new value after a percentage change
   • work out the increase and add it to the original amount, or
   • work out the decrease and subtract it from the original amount.

7 To write one quantity as a percentage of another:
- write one quantity as a fraction of the other
- change the fraction to a decimal
- multiply the decimal by 100%

8 Profit (or loss) is the difference between the cost price and the selling price.

If a profit is made:

selling price = cost price + profit

If a loss is made:

selling price = cost price − loss

9 Percentage profit $= \dfrac{\text{profit}}{\text{cost price}} \times 100\%$

10 Percentage loss $= \dfrac{\text{loss}}{\text{cost price}} \times 100\%$

11 Simple interest over several years is when the sum of money invested (or borrowed) remains the same over those years and when the percentage rate of interest remains the same over those years.

7 Shape and measure

The circle is one of the most important shapes in maths.

Oil pipelines have circular cross-sections because the circle has a larger area than any other shape with the same perimeter.

7.1 Circles

Different parts of the circle have special names:

	The perimeter of a circle is called the **circumference**.
	A straight line crossing a circle is called a **chord**.
	A section of the circumference is called an **arc**.
	A straight line from the centre of a circle to the edge is called a **radius**.
	A straight line crossing a circle through the centre is called a **diameter**.
	The region of a circle contained by two radius lines and an arc is called a **sector**.
	A straight line that touches a circle is called a **tangent**.
	The region of a circle contained by a chord and an arc is called a **segment**.

Exercise 7A

1 Write down the correct names for **(a)**, **(b)** and **(c)**:

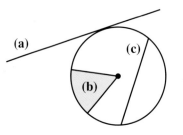

2 Give examples of a segment, arc, chord and radius in this diagram:

3 Draw a circle using your compasses.

   (a) Use a ruler to draw a chord, a tangent and two radii.

   (b) Shade in and label a sector and a segment.

radii is the plural of radius. It is pronounced *ray-dee-eye*.

7.2 Circle constructions

You can use a ruler and compasses to draw shapes accurately. An accurate drawing like this is called a **construction**.

Example 1

Construct this shape using ruler and compasses.

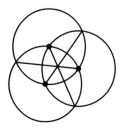

Set your compasses to 3 cm. Leave them set like this throughout. Draw the first circle …

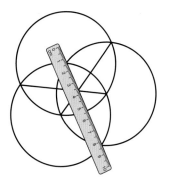

… and draw another circle through the centre.

Draw the third circle through the centre of the other two.

Use a ruler to draw the lines.

Exercise 7B

Construct these shapes using ruler and compasses. The red lines show you what to draw first.

1

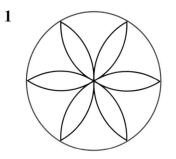

Hint: Keep your compasses set at 3 cm.

2

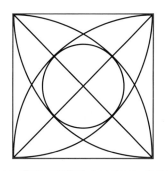

Hint: Draw the small circle last.

3

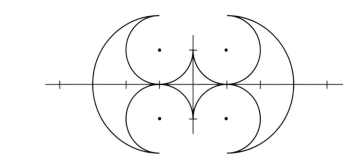

4

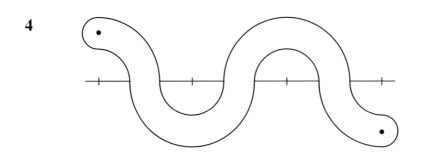

7.3 Diagonals

When constructing shapes you sometimes join points together with a straight line.

■   **The lines that join opposite corners of a quadrilateral are called diagonals.**

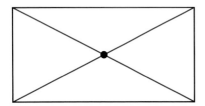

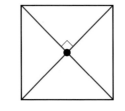

Bisect means to cut in half.

The diagonals of a rectangle are the same length and meet at the centre.

The diagonals of a square bisect each other at right-angles.

■   **The diagonals of polygons are lines that join corners that are not next to each other.**

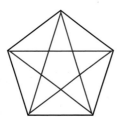

A pentagon has five diagonals.

Exercise 7C

You will need **Activity sheet 1**.

1   (a)   Draw in the diagonals of these quadrilaterals.

(b)   Draw the quadrilaterals with these diagonals.

(c)   Measure the lengths and angles. What can you say about the diagonals of:

(i) a square   (ii) a kite   (iii) a rhombus.

2 Draw all the diagonals of a regular hexagon.
Shade in and label:

   (a) a kite

   (b) an isosceles triangle

   (c) a right-angled triangle.

3 Investigation

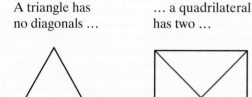

A triangle has no diagonals ...   ... a quadrilateral has two ...   ... and a pentagon has five.

Investigate the number of diagonals for different polygons.

7.4 More constructions

You can use circle properties in constructions.

Example 2

Construct a triangle with sides of length 4 cm, 5 cm and 6 cm.

Draw the longest side using a ruler.   Set the compasses to 5 cm. Draw an arc like this: Set the compasses to 4 cm. Draw another arc like this: Join the ends of the line to the point where the arcs cross.

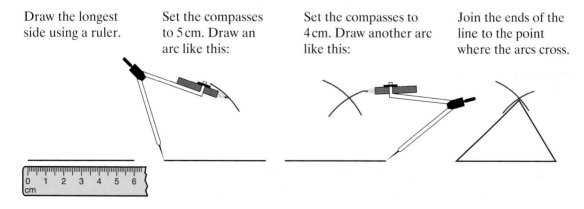

Example 3

Complete this rhombus. Two sides have already been drawn.

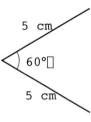

Open your compasses to the length of one side.

Draw an arc with the centre at an unjoined end.

Draw an arc with the centre at the other unjoined end.

Join up the lines.

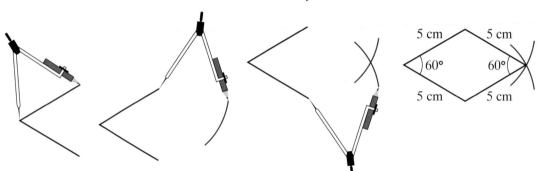

Exercise 7D

1 Construct triangles with sides of length:

    (a) 5 cm, 5 cm, 8 cm   **(b)** 4 cm, 7 cm, 9 cm

    (c) 3 cm, 4 cm, 5 cm   **(d)** 4 cm, 4 cm, 4 cm

2 Draw these angles using a ruler and protractor. Complete each one to form a rhombus.

(a)   **(b)**

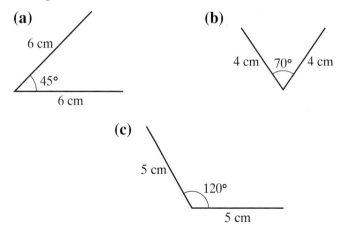

3 Construct these shapes using ruler and compasses.

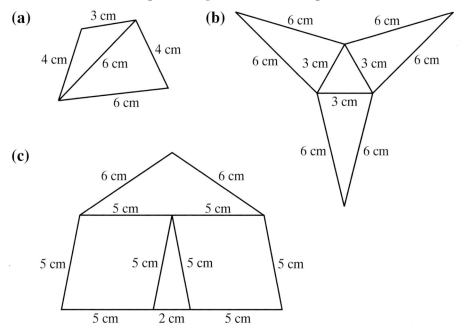

(a)   (b)   (c)

7.5 Bisecting an angle

The red line divides this angle exactly in half. It is
called the bisector of the angle.

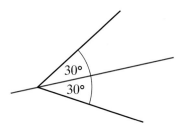

You can construct the bisector of an angle using
ruler and compasses.

Example 4

Construct the bisector of this angle:

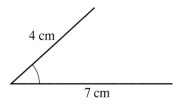

4 cm

7 cm

Open your compasses to 3 cm. Leave them set like this throughout.

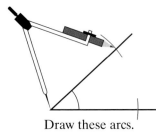 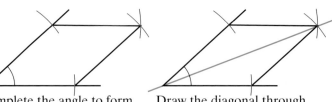

Draw these arcs.   Complete the angle to form a rhombus.   Draw the diagonal through the original angle.

The diagonal you have drawn is the bisector of the angle.

Exercise 7E

You will need **Activity sheet 2**.

1 For each angle:
   • open your compasses to the length shown
   • construct the bisector of the angle

2 Construct the bisector of each angle.

> Hint: In **2** you will need to choose a suitable length to open your compasses to for each angle.

7.6 Perpendicular lines

Perpendicular lines meet at right angles.

The green line is the **perpendicular bisector** of the black one.

Exercise 7F

Use a ruler and compasses with **Activity sheet 3**.

1 Draw arcs to construct perpendicular bisectors to each line. The first one has been done for you.

2 Construct perpendiculars to each line **through** the point shown. The first one has been done for you.

3 Construct perpendiculars to each line **at** the point shown. The first one has been done for you.

7.7 Solid shapes

Many objects are constructed from solid mathematical shapes.

The cooling towers on this power station are a special mathematical shape called a catenoid.

You should be familiar with cuboids, cubes, pyramids and prisms. You also need to be able to recognize these common solids.

	A prism with a constant circular cross-section is called a **cylinder**.
	A pyramid with a circular base is called a **cone**.
	A ball-shape is called a **sphere**.
	Half of a sphere is called a **hemisphere**.

Faces, edges and vertices

Solid shapes have faces, edges and vertices.

Vertices is the plural of vertex.

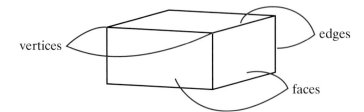

- **A face is a surface on the outside of a solid shape.**
- **An edge is the line where two faces meet.**
- **A vertex is the corner where three or more faces meet.**

Example 5

Write down all the faces, edges and vertices on this triangular prism.

The faces are ABC, ABED, BCFE, ACFD and DEF.

The edges are AB, AC, BC, AD, BE, CF, ED, EF and DF.

The vertices are A, B, C, D, E and F.

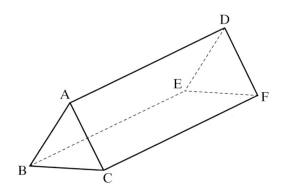

Exercise 7G

1 Give the mathematical names of the shapes that make these objects.

(a)

(b)

(c)

2 How many faces, edges and vertices are there on each of these shapes?

(a)   (b)   (c)

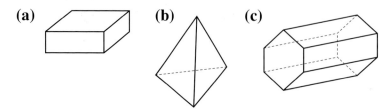

3 How many faces, edges and vertices are there in:

(a) a sphere   (b) a cylinder.

Hint: look at the definitions on page 124.

4 This shape is a pentagonal prism.

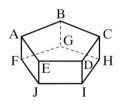

Write down:

(a) an edge that is parallel to BC
(b) a face that is parallel to ABCDE
(c) all the faces that are perpendicular to ABCDE
(d) an edge that is perpendicular to IJ.

Remember: Parallel means in the same direction.
Perpendicular means at right-angles.

7.8 Nets

Robina and Supraj are making dice.

Robina cuts out this shape …   … and folds it up …   … to make a cube.

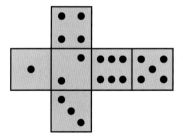

Supraj cuts out this shape …   … but he can't fold it up to make a cube.

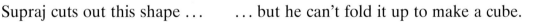

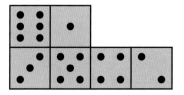

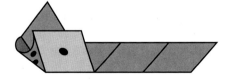

■ **A flat shape that can be folded to make a solid shape is called a net.**

Example 6

Here are Robina and Supraj's shapes. Which could be the net of a cube?

(a) 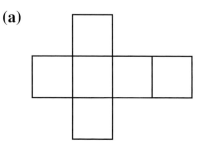   **(b)**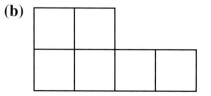

(a) This shape can be folded to make a cube. It is the net of a cube.

(b) This shape can't be folded to make a cube. It is not the net of a cube.

Exercise 7H

1 Draw these shapes on squared paper and cut them out. Which of them could be the net of a cube?

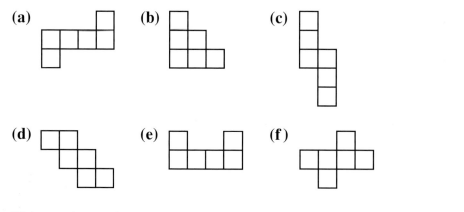

(a)   **(b)**   **(c)**

(d)   **(e)**   **(f)**

2 Using ruler and compasses construct this net on thin card. Add the tabs shown and cut it out. Make the net into a solid shape by sticking down the tabs. Write down the mathematical name of your shape.

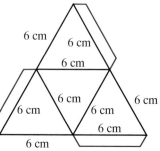

6 cm 6 cm 6 cm 6 cm 6 cm 6 cm 6 cm 6 cm 6 cm

3 Draw a sketch of the solid shape each of these nets will make. If possible, give each shape its mathematical name.

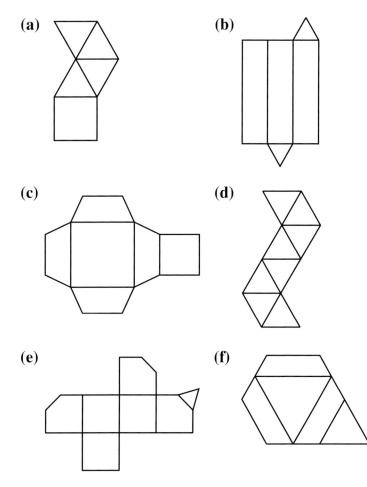

(a)

(b)

(c)

(d)

(e)

(f)

4 Use ruler and compasses to construct a net for each of these solids.

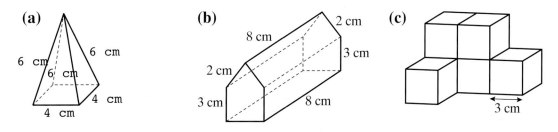

(a)

6 cm 6 cm 6 cm 4 cm 4 cm

(b)

8 cm 2 cm 3 cm 2 cm 3 cm 8 cm

(c)

3 cm

5 Sketch four *different* nets for a square based pyramid.

6 Which mathematical solids could these shapes be nets for?

(a) 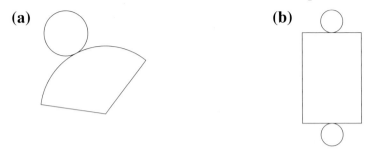 **(b)**

7.9 Plan and elevation

Architects and designers often represent three-dimensional objects with two-dimensional drawings.

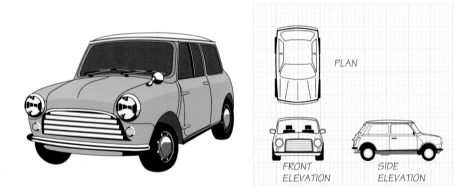

- **The plan of a solid is the view when seen from above.**
- **The front elevation is the view when seen from the front.**
- **The side elevation is the view when seen from the side.**

Example 7

Draw the plan and elevations of this shape.

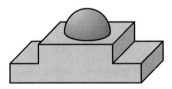

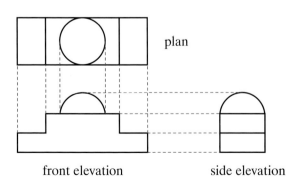

plan

front elevation   side elevation

You should draw plans and elevations using dotted lines to show how the different drawings match up.

Exercise 7I

1 Sketch the plans and elevations of these shapes.

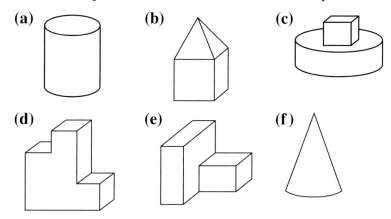

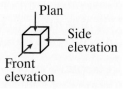

2 Use multilink cubes to construct these solids. Sketch each one.

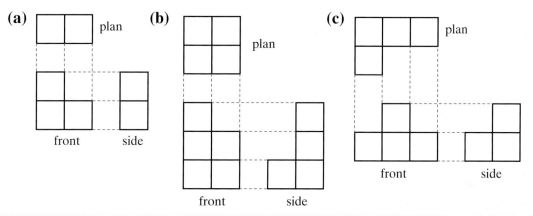

3 Investigation

Can you describe solids with these plans and elevations?

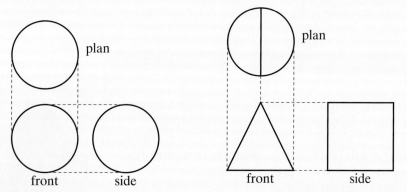

Draw your own set of three shapes. Try to describe a solid which has your shapes as its plan, front elevation and side elevation.

7.10 Metric and imperial measure

Most measurements taken today are in metric units. It is important to be able to convert metric units into old style imperial units like miles and pints.

In September 1999 the NASA Mars Climate Orbiter was lost in space because some of the designers forgot to convert metric to imperial units. It was worth $125 million.

Metric		**Imperial**
8 kilometres	=	5 miles
1 kilogram	=	2.2 pounds
1 litre	=	1.75 pints
2.54 centimetres	=	1 inch

You can write lb for pounds and ″ for inches.

Example 8

Katie weighs 68 kg. What is her weight in pounds?

$1\,\text{kg} = 2.2\,\text{lb}$
$68\,\text{kg} = 68 \times 2.2 = 149.6\,\text{lb}$

Example 9

A bathtub holds 170 pints of water. How much can it hold in litres? Give your answer to one decimal place.

$1.75\,\text{pints} = 1\,\text{litre}$
$1\,\text{pint} = 1 \div 1.75\,\text{litres}$
$170\,\text{pints} = 170 \times (1 \div 1.75) = 97.1\,\text{litres}$

Exercise 7J

1 An African elephant weighs 12 800 lb. What is its weight in kilograms? Give your answer to the nearest 10 kg.

2 The radius of the earth is 6360 km. What is this in miles?

3 Change these distances to miles.

(a) 32 km   (b) 208 km   (c) 3680 km
(d) 136 km   (e) 9776 km   (f) 2400 km

4 Change these distances to kilometres.

    (a) 25 miles   **(b)** 1275 miles   **(c)** 1000 miles

    (d) 220 miles   **(e)** 600 miles   **(f)** 445 miles

5 A reservoir holds 11 million litres of water. How much can it hold in pints?

6 Change these lengths to centimetres. Give your answers to 2 decimal places.

> There are 12 inches in a foot.

    (a) 12″   **(b)** 2″   **(c)** $6\frac{1}{2}″$

    (d) 3 ft   **(e)** 1 ft 6″   **(f)** $2\frac{2}{3}$ ft

7 Change these lengths to feet and inches. Give your answers to the nearest inch.

    (a) 8 cm   **(b)** 110 cm   **(c)** 12 cm

    (d) 30 cm   **(e)** 68 cm   **(f)** 80 cm

8 Copy and complete this table showing the top speeds of some animals in miles per hour and kilometres per hour.

Animal	Top speed (mph)	Top speed (kph)
Penguin		40
Peregrine falcon	225	
Greyhound	38	
Cheetah		110
Swordfish	56	
Bumblebee		12

Summary of key points

1 Different parts of the circle have special names:

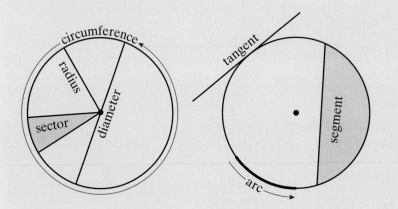

2 An accurate drawing using ruler and compasses is called a construction.

3 The lines that join opposite corners of a quadrilateral are called diagonals.

4 The diagonals of a polygon are lines that join corners that are not next to each other.

5 A perpendicular bisector cuts a line in half at right angles.

6

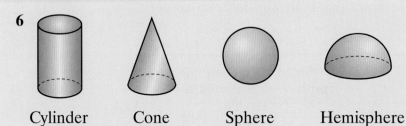

| Cylinder | Cone | Sphere | Hemisphere |

7
- A face is a surface on the outside of a solid shape.
- An edge is the line where two faces meet.
- A vertex is the corner where three or more faces meet.

8 A flat shape that can be folded to make a solid shape is called a net.

The net of a cube.

9
- The plan of a solid is the view when seen from above.
- The front elevation is the view when seen from the front.
- The side elevation is the view when seen from the side.

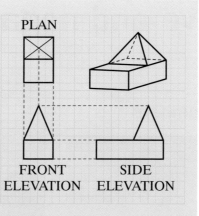

PLAN

FRONT
ELEVATION

SIDE
ELEVATION

10

Metric		Imperial
8 kilometres	=	5 miles
1 kilogram	=	2.2 pounds
1 litre	=	1.75 pints
2.54 centimetres	=	1 inch

8 Positive and negative numbers

8.1 Ordering numbers

The highest peak in the Sierra Nevada mountain range in California is Mount Whitney. It is 4544 m above sea level.

Death Valley in California is the lowest land in the Western hemisphere. It is 84 m below sea level, which can be written as −84 m.

- ■ **Positive numbers are greater than zero.**

- ■ **Negative numbers are less than zero. They are written with a minus sign in front of the number.**

You can use a horizontal number line to answer questions about positive and negative numbers.

Example 1

Write down these numbers in order of size, starting with the smallest:

4, 0, −4, −7, −2, 3, −5, −9.

The order is −9, −7, −5, −4, −2, 0, 3, 4.

Example 2

Write down all the whole numbers that are bigger than −7, smaller than 6 and are odd.

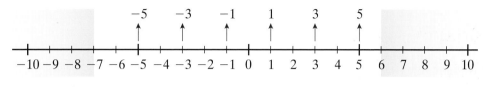

The numbers are −5, −3, −1, 1, 3 and 5.

−7 is not included because the numbers must be bigger than −7.

Exercise 8A

Use a number line to answer these questions.

1   Write these numbers in order of size, starting with the smallest:

(a) 5, −7, −1, −4, 8, −3.
(b) 6, −3, 3, −4, 2, −9.
(c) −5, 4, −8, 2, −4, −3.
(d) 2, −8, 1, −3, −7, −4.
(e) −18, 2, −9, −13, −5, −12.
(f) −5, 1, −12, −23, −9, −26.

2   Write down all the numbers that are larger than −9, smaller than 4 and are odd.

3   Abi chose a number that is smaller than −5, larger than −8 and is even. What number did Abi choose?

4   Write down all the numbers that are smaller than 10, larger than −8 and are multiples of 3.

8.2 Using the number line

You can answer questions by moving up or down the number line.

Example 3

Use a number line to find the number that is:

(a) 3 more than −5

(b) 6 less than 2

(a) You have 3 more so the number gets bigger.

Start at −5 and move 3 spaces to the right

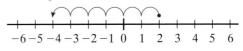

The answer is −2.

(b) You have 6 less so the number gets smaller.

Start at 2 and move 6 spaces to the left

The answer is −4.

Example 4

Write down the next two numbers in this pattern

9, 5, 1, −3, …

The numbers go down by 4 each time.

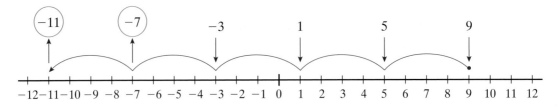

The next two numbers in the pattern are −7 and −11.

Exercise 8B

Use a number line to answer these questions.

1 Find the number that is:

    (a) 3 more than 2   **(b)** 5 more than −3

    (c) 3 less than −4   **(d)** 7 less than 3

    (e) 7 more than −3   **(f)** 3 less than 0

    (g) 6 more than −5   **(h)** 4 less than −5

    (i) 7 more than −7   **(j)** 9 less than 2

    (k) 3 more than −8   **(l)** 7 less than −3

2 What number is 9 more than the result of 3 less than -2?

3 Write down the next two numbers in each pattern:
  (a) 10, 7, 4, 1, ...   **(b)** 5, 3, 1, -1, ...
  (c) $-10, -7, -4, -1, ...$ **(d)** $-11, -7, -3, 1, ...$
  (e) $-9, -8, -6, -3, ...$ **(f)** 13, 11, 7, 1, ...

4 Work out the two missing numbers in each number pattern:
  (a) 14, 11, 8, 5, ☐, ☐, -4.
  (b) $-13, -9, -5, -1,$ ☐, ☐, 11.
  (c) 15, 11, 7, 3, ☐, ☐, -9.
  (d) $-16, -11, -6, -1,$ ☐, ☐, 14.
  (e) $-12, -11, -9, -6,$ ☐, ☐, 9.
  (f) 19, 17, 13, 7, ☐, ☐, -23.

8.3 Adding and subtracting positive and negative numbers

You can use number tables to add and subtract positive and negative numbers.

Example 5

Use number tables to find the answers.

(a) $1 + -3$

(b) $2 - -1$

(a)

First Number

+	3	2	1	0	−1	−2	−3
3	6	5	4	3	2	1	0
2	5	4	3	2	1	0	−1
1	4	3	2	1	0	−1	−2
0	3	2	1	0	−1	−2	−3
−1	2	1	0	−1	−2	−3	−4
−2	1	0	−1	−2	−3	−4	−5
−3	0	−1	−2	−3	−4	−5	−6

Second Number

$1 + -3 = -2$

(b)

First Number

−	3	2	1	0	−1	−2	−3
3	0	−1	−2	−3	−4	−5	−6
2	1	0	−1	−2	−3	−4	−5
1	2	1	0	−1	−2	−3	−4
0	3	2	1	0	−1	−2	−3
−1	4	3	2	1	0	−1	−2
−2	5	4	3	2	1	0	−1
−3	6	5	4	3	2	1	0

Second Number

$2 - -1 = 3$

■ **If you add a negative number the result is smaller.**

answer goes down

■ **If you subtract a negative number the result is bigger.**

answer goes up

Example 6

Use the rules above to find the answers.

(a) $4 + -7$ **(b)** $-2 - -3$

(a) $4 + -7$ **(b)** $-2 - -3$

Start at 4   + − ↓   **answer** goes down

Start at −2   − − ↑   **answer** goes up

So $4 + -7 = 4 - 7 = -3$ So $-2 - -3 = -2 + 3 = 1$

Exercise 8C

1 Use the number tables in **Example 5** to find the answers:

   (a) $3 + -2$ **(b)** $-2 + -2$

   (c) $-3 + 2$ **(d)** $-3 - -2$

   (e) $-3 - 1$ **(f)** $1 - -2$

Use the rules shown to answer these questions:

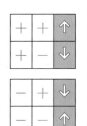

answer goes up

answer goes down

answer goes down

goes up

2 **(a)** $-5 - 2$ **(b)** $-6 + -3$

    (c) $2 - 6$ **(d)** $-7 - -2$

    (e) $8 - -3$ **(f)** $-3 + 2$

    (g) $9 + -2$ **(h)** $-4 - -5$

    (i) $-3 + -2$ **(j)** $-6 - -2$

    (k) $-3 - -5$ **(l)** $7 - -4$

3 **(a)** $8 - -2$ **(b)** $4 - -9$

    (c) $8 - -6$ **(d)** $-4 - -9$

    (e) $-8 - -4$ **(f)** $-9 - -1$

    (g) $-4 + 9$ **(h)** $-9 - 2$

    (i) $-3 - -6$ **(j)** $-2 + -7$

    (k) $-6 + 1$ **(l)** $+8 - 2$

4 (a) $-3 + 4 - 6$ **(b)** $-4 + -5 - 2$

   (c) $2 - -9 + -4$ **(d)** $-6 - 5 + -3$

   (e) $9 + -3 - -7$ **(f)** $-4 + -9 - 5$

5 Check your answers to questions **1** to **4** using a calculator.

8.4 Multiplying positive and negative numbers

You already know how to multiply positive numbers.

■ **A positive number multiplied by a positive number is a positive number.**

First number	×	Second number	=
+		+	+

This plane is landing.

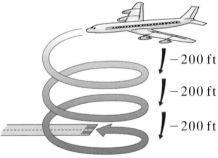

Each turn it gets 200 feet lower.

You can write this as -200 feet.

In total it goes

$-200\text{ft} + -200\text{ft} + -200\text{ft} = -600\text{ft}.$

You can write this as $-200\text{ft} \times 3 = -600\text{ft}$

and so $-200 \times 3 = -600.$

■ **A negative number multiplied by a positive number is a negative number.**

First number	×	Second number	=
−		+	−

$-200\,\text{ft} \times 3$ has the same value as

$3 \times -200\,\text{ft}$, so $-200 \times 3 = -600$

and $3 \times -200 = -600$.

Remember: you can multiply in any order. For example:

$6 \times 2 = 2 \times 6 = 12$

This is called **commutativity**.

■ **A positive number multiplied by a negative number is a negative number.**

First number	×	Second number	=
+		−	−

You can use a number line to help with multiplying negative numbers.

Example 7

Use a number line to work out -4×3.

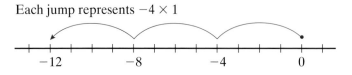

You have moved back 12 spaces to $-4 \times 3 = -12$.

You can make -1 jump of -4 on the number line by reversing 1 jump.

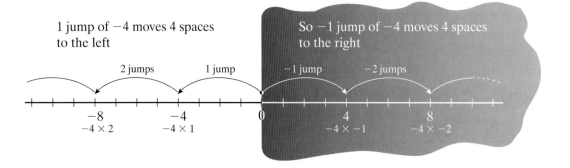

So $-4 \times -1 - 4$ and $-4 \times -2 = 8$.

■ **A negative number multiplied by a negative number is a positive number.**

First number	×	Second number	=
−		−	+

Example 8

Use the rules of multiplication to work out:

(a) -2×6 **(b)** -4×-3

(a) $-2 \quad \times \quad 6 \quad = -12$ **(b)** $-4 \quad \times \quad -3 \quad = 12$

First number	×	Second number	=	
−		+	−	answer is negative

First number	×	Second number	=	
−		−	+	answer is positive

Exercise 8D

1 The temperature in Athens fell by 2°C (a change of −2°C) each day for a week. What is the change of temperature over the whole week?

2

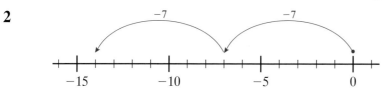

Use this number line to work out −7 × 2.

3 Use number lines to work out:

    (a) −3 × 3   **(b)** 6 × −2

4

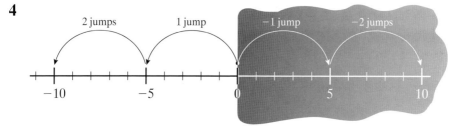

Use this number line to work out −5 × −2.

5 Use the rules of multiplication to work out:

(a) 2 × −3	**(b)** −5 × 5
(c) 5 × −4	**(d)** −2 × −2
(e) 1 × 1	**(f)** 1 × −5
(g) −6 × 3	**(h)** −3 × −4
(i) 5 × −3	**(j)** 5 × 4
(k) −8 × −3	**(l)** −4 × −6
(m) −3 × 7	**(n)** −4 × −3
(o) −7 × −4	**(p)** −4 × 8
(q) 6 × 7	**(r)** 7 × −5
(s) −9 × 3	**(t)** −6 × −8

First number	×	Second number	=
+		+	+
+		−	−
−		+	−
−		−	+

6 Work out:

   (a) $(2 \times -4) \times -3$ **(b)** $(-5 \times 2) \times -3$

   (c) $(5 \times -4) \times 2$

> Remember:
> work out the
> brackets first.

7 Work out:

   (a) $2 \times (-4 \times -3)$ **(b)** $-5 \times (2 \times -3)$

   (c) $5 \times (-4 \times 2)$

8 What do you notice about your answers to questions **6** and **7**?

8.5 Dividing positive and negative numbers

You already know how to divide positive numbers.

■ **A positive number divided by a positive number is a positive number.**

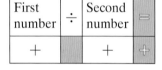

You can use a number line to help with dividing negative numbers.

Example 9

Use a number line to work out $-6 \div 3$.

If you divide -6 into 3 equal parts, how big is each part?

> Remember: you
> can write $-6 \div 3$
>
> as $\dfrac{-6}{3}$

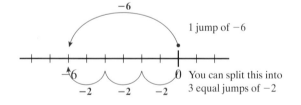

So $-6 \div 3 = -2$.

■ **A negative number divided by a positive number is a negative number.**

First number	$\div$	Second number	$=$
$-$		$+$	$-$

You can think about division in a different way.

Example 10

Use a number line to work out $-8 \div -4$.

How many lots of -4 go into -8?

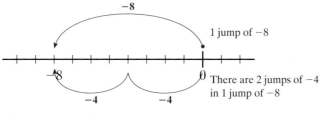

So $-8 \div -4 = 2$.

■ **A negative number divided by a negative number is a positive number.**

First number	÷	Second number	=
−		−	+

You can divide by a negative number by starting with a suitable multiplication.

Example 11

Work out $20 \div -5$ by finding a suitable multiplication.

What number fits into this equation?

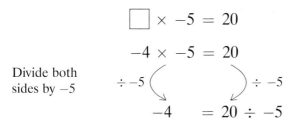

$$\square \times -5 = 20$$

$$-4 \times -5 = 20$$

Divide both sides by -5

$$-4 = 20 \div -5$$

Remember: dividing is the **inverse** operation to multiplying, so
$$-4 \times -5 \div -5 = -4$$

So $20 \div -5 = -4$.

■ **A positive number divided by a negative number is a negative number.**

First number	÷	Second number	=
+		−	−

Example 12

Use the rules of division to work out:

(a) $-27 \div -3$ **(b)** $35 \div -5$

(a) $-27 \div -3 = 9$ **(b)** $35 \div -5 = -7$

First number	÷	Second number	=
−		−	+

answer is positive

First number	÷	Second number	=
+		−	−

answer is negative

Exercise 8E

1 A tower is 200 feet high. Natalie abseils at a steady rate down the side of the tower (a change in height of -200 feet) in 100 seconds.
What is the change in height each second?

2

-15

-15 — — — — — 0

? ? ? ? ?

Copy this diagram and fill in the number you think should go where the question marks are.
What is $-15 \div 5$?

3 Use a number line to work out:

(a) $-14 \div 2$ **(b)** $-10 \div 5$
(c) $-8 \div 2$ **(d)** $-12 \div 6$
(e) $-9 \div 3$ **(f)** $-20 \div 4$

4 Copy and complete these equations:

(a) $\boxed{} \times -6 = 12$ **(b)** $\boxed{} \times -3 = 21$
(c) $\boxed{} \times -6 = -24$

5 Use your answers to question **4** to find the answers:

(a) $12 \div -6$ (b) $21 \div -3$

(c) $-24 \div -6$

6 Use the rules of division to work out:

First number	$\div$	Second number	$=$
$+$		$+$	$+$
$+$		$-$	$-$
$-$		$+$	$-$
$-$		$-$	$+$

(a) $-40 \div 8$ (b) $-36 \div -4$

(c) $48 \div -6$ (d) $-18 \div -2$

(e) $-24 \div 12$ (f) $-27 \div -3$

(g) $30 \div -6$ (h) $-16 \div -2$

(i) $45 \div -5$

7 Use any of the methods in this chapter to work out:

(a) $36 \div -3$ (b) $-49 \div -7$

(c) $-28 \div 4$ (d) $-72 \div -9$

(e) $26 \div -2$ (f) $-21 \div 7$

(g) $-2 \times (-6 + 3)$ (h) $(-7 - -3) \times 7$

(i) $(2 - 9) \times -4$ (j) $(-22 - 8) \div 6$

(k) $(-7 + -5) \div -3$ (l) $(31 + -7) \div -8$

Summary of key points

1 Positive numbers are greater than zero.

2 Negative numbers are less than zero. They are written with a minus sign in front of the number.

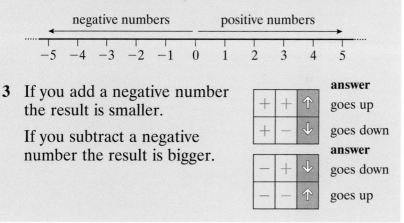

3 If you add a negative number the result is smaller.

If you subtract a negative number the result is bigger.

4 A positive number multiplied by a positive number is a positive number.
A positive number multiplied by a negative number is a negative number.
A negative number multiplied by a positive number is a negative number.
A negative number multiplied by a negative number is a positive number.

First number	×	Second number	=
+		+	+
+		−	−
−		+	−
−		−	+

5 A positive number divided by a positive number is a positive number.
A positive number divided by a negative number is a negative number.
A negative number divided by a positive number is a negative number.
A negative number divided by a negative number is a positive number.

First number	÷	Second number	=
+		+	+
+		−	−
−		+	−
−		−	+

9 Number patterns

9.1 Patterns from pictures

Here are the first four shapes in a dot pattern.

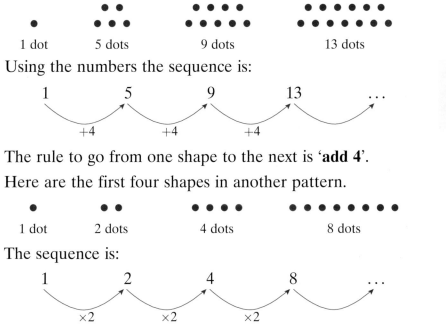

A sequence is the name given to a number pattern.

The rule to go from one shape to the next is '**add 4**'.

Here are the first four shapes in another pattern.

The sequence is:

The rule to go from one term to the next is '**multiply by 2**'.

Exercise 9A

Copy the following shape patterns.
For each pattern
● draw the next 2 shapes
● write down the pattern using numbers
● write down the rule to go from one shape to the next.

1

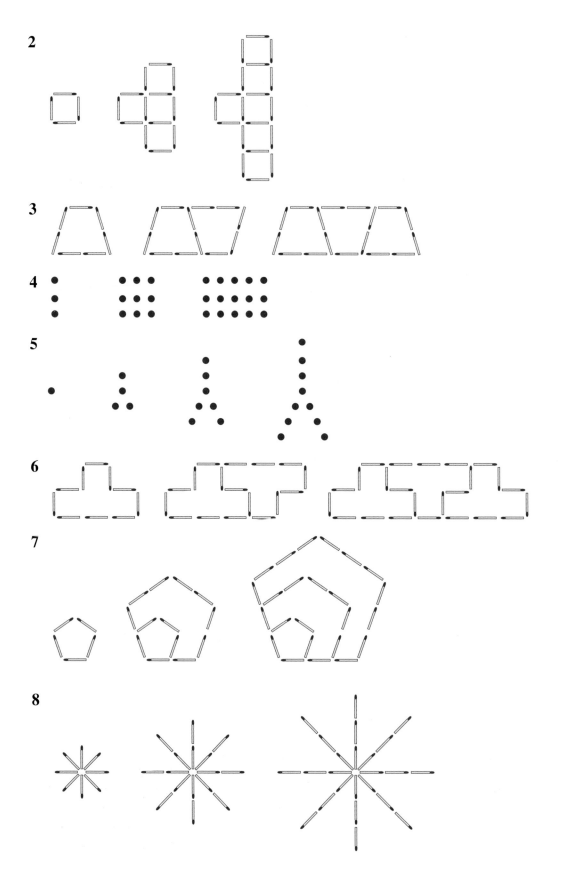

9.2 Number machines

A number machine performs an operation on a number.
You can use number machines to make number patterns.

Example 1

Input the numbers 1, 2, 3, 4 into this one-step number machine.

×7

input	output
1 →	7
2 →	14
3 →	21
4 →	28

$1 - 1 = 0$ ➤ $0 \times 2 = 0$
$2 - 1 = 1$ ➤ $1 \times 2 = 2$

and so on …

Example 2

This two-step number machine performs the operation -1 followed by the operation $\times 2$:

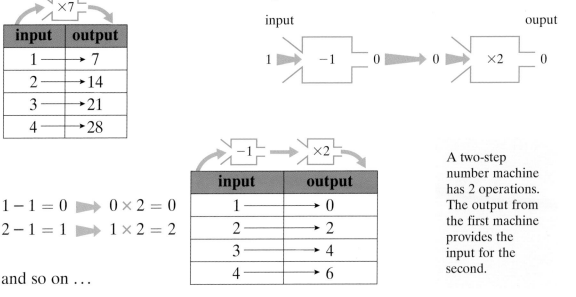

input   ouput

1 ➤ −1 0 ➤ 0 ➤ ×2 0

−1 ➤ ×2

input	output
1 →	0
2 →	2
3 →	4
4 →	6

A two-step number machine has 2 operations. The output from the first machine provides the input for the second.

Exercise 9B

1 For each question
   - copy and complete the table to show the output numbers
   - describe the pattern for the output numbers.

The first one has been done for you.

(a) 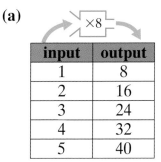 ×8

input	output
1	8
2	16
3	24
4	32
5	40

(b) ÷5

input	output
15	
20	
25	
30	
35	

(c) ×11

input	output
4	
5	
6	
7	
8	

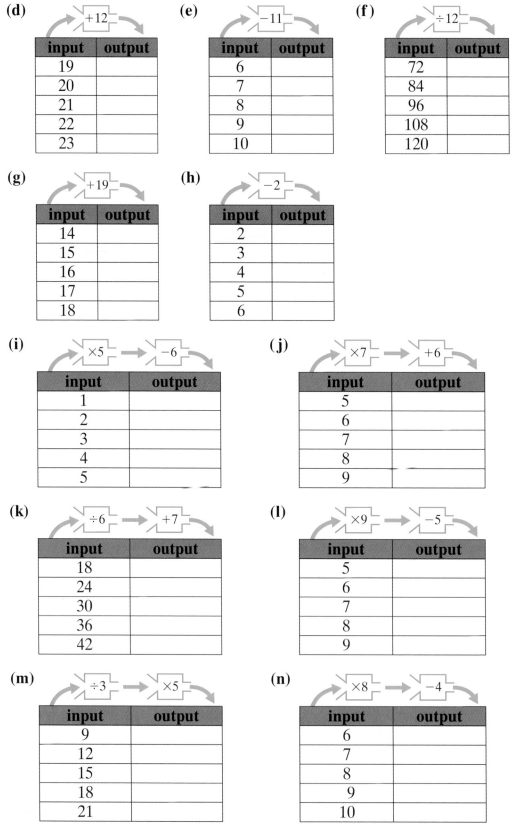

(d) +12

input	output
19	
20	
21	
22	
23	

(e) −11

input	output
6	
7	
8	
9	
10	

(f) ÷12

input	output
72	
84	
96	
108	
120	

(g) +19

input	output
14	
15	
16	
17	
18	

(h) −2

input	output
2	
3	
4	
5	
6	

(i) ×5 → −6

input	output
1	
2	
3	
4	
5	

(j) ×7 → +6

input	output
5	
6	
7	
8	
9	

(k) ÷6 → +7

input	output
18	
24	
30	
36	
42	

(l) ×9 → −5

input	output
5	
6	
7	
8	
9	

(m) ÷3 → ×5

input	output
9	
12	
15	
18	
21	

(n) ×8 → −4

input	output
6	
7	
8	
9	
10	

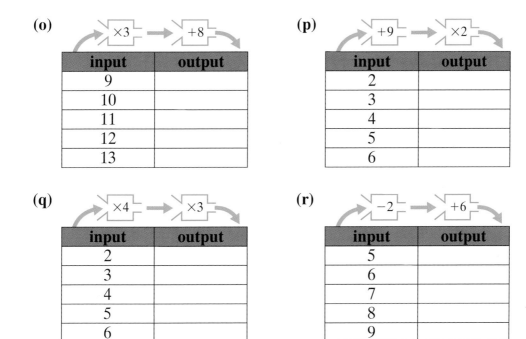

(o)

×3 → +8

input	output
9	
10	
11	
12	
13	

(p)

+9 → ×2

input	output
2	
3	
4	
5	
6	

(q)

×4 → ×3

input	output
2	
3	
4	
5	
6	

(r)

−2 → +6

input	output
5	
6	
7	
8	
9	

Exercise 9C

1 For each question complete the table to show the missing inputs or outputs.

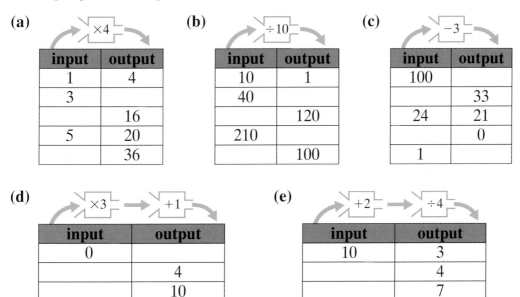

(a)

×4

input	output
1	4
3	
	16
5	20
	36

(b)

÷10

input	output
10	1
40	
	120
210	
	100

(c)

−3

input	output
100	
	33
24	21
	0
1	

(d)

×3 → +1

input	output
0	
	4
	10
5	16
10	

(e)

+2 → ÷4

input	output
10	3
	4
	7
34	
98	

(f)

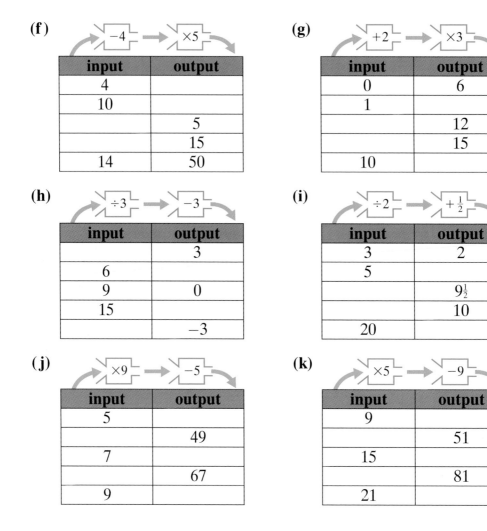

input	output
4	
10	
	5
	15
14	50

(g)

input	output
0	6
1	
	12
	15
10	

(h)

input	output
	3
6	
9	0
15	
	−3

(i)

input	output
3	2
5	
	9½
	10
20	

(j)

input	output
5	
	49
7	
	67
9	

(k)

input	output
9	
	51
15	
	81
21	

9.3 Inverse operations

input ➤ ×3 ⟶ −1 ➤ output

Given an input value of 2, to find the output value ×3 then −1. The output value is 5.

2 ➤ ×3 ➤ 6 ➤ −1 ➤ 5

If you are given an output value, you have to complete the inverse operation to find the input value.

So if 11 was the output value

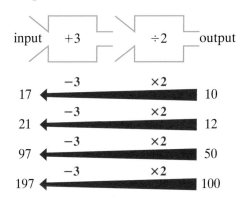

4 must have been the input value.

Example 3

Find the input values by using the
correct inverse operation.

Use this table to help find
the inverse:

Operation	Inverse
+	−
−	+
×	÷
÷	×

9.4 Sequences

Input the terms 1, 2, 3 and 4 into this two-step number machine:

input	output
1	4
2	7
3	10
4	13
5	16

The output numbers form a sequence

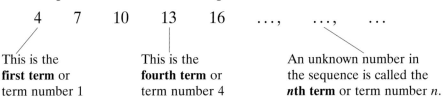

4   7   10   13   16   …,   …,   …

This is the
first term or
term number 1

This is the
fourth term or
term number 4

An unknown number in
the sequence is called the
nth term or term number *n*.

When exploring number sequences you can find:

■ **a rule to find the next term**

■ **a rule to find the *n*th term.**

Look at the sequence produced by the two-stage operation: ×3 then add 1.

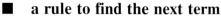

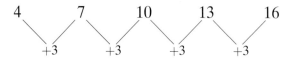

The difference between each pair of terms is 3.

To find the next term in this sequence add 3:

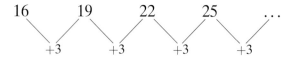

The difference between consecutive terms is +3.

The next term is 28 and the rule is **+3**.

In finding the rule for the next term it is a good idea to look at the differences between each pair of terms.

Example 4

Find the next two terms in the sequence:

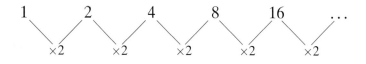

This time you have to ×2 to get the next term.

The next term is 16 and the rule is **×2**.

Exercise 9D

1 Copy each sequence and find the missing terms, writing the rule you used.

(a) 1, 5, 9, 13, ...   (b) 7, 14, 21, ...
(c) 30, 24, 18, ...   (d) 11, 22, ..., ..., 55, 66
(e) 20, 17, 14, ..., ...   (f) 7, 14, ..., ..., 35, 42
(g) 39, 33, 27, ..., 15, ... (h) 8, 6, 4, ..., ..., −2
(i) 18, 9, 0, −9, ..., ...   (j) 2, 5, 8, ..., ..., 17

(k) $\frac{1}{2}$, 1, $1\frac{1}{2}$, 2, ..., ..., ... **(l)** 24, 12, 6, ..., ..., ...

(m) $1\frac{1}{2}$, 3, $4\frac{1}{2}$, ..., ..., ... **(n)** 64, 32, ..., ..., 4, ..., ...

(o) 1, 3, 9, 27, ..., ..., ... **(p)** 1, 4, 16, ..., ..., ...

(q) 1000, 100, ..., ..., ... **(r)** 72, 36, 18, ..., ..., ...

(s) 1, 3, 6, 10, ..., ..., ... **(t)** 4, 7, 11, 16, 22, ..., ...

(u) 10, 30, 90, ..., ..., ... **(v)** 1, 1, 2, 3, 5, 8, ..., ..., ...

9.5 Find the *n*th term

■ **You can use algebra to write a general rule which allows you to find any term in a sequence. This is also called the *n*th term rule.**

Example 5

Find the **general rule** for this sequence:

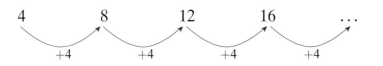

The next term is 20 and the rule for the next term is +4.

■ **To help find the general rule, write the term numbers and sequence in a table.**

Term number	Sequence
1 —×4→ 4	
2 —×4→ 8	
3 —×4→ 12	
4 —×4→ 16	
⋮	⋮
10 —×4→ 40	
⋮	⋮
100 —×4→ 400	
⋮	
n —×4→ 4*n*	

+4
+4
+4

The difference between consecutive terms is +4

This is the tenth term

This is the hundredth term

This is the general rule

Exercise 9E

These sequences have been generated by one-step machines.

1 For each sequence, find:
- the missing terms
- the difference between consecutive terms
- the general rule.

(a)

Term number	Sequence
1 ⟶	12
2 ⟶	13
3 ⟶	14
⋮	⋮
10 ⟶	
⋮	⋮
100 ⟶	
⋮	⋮
n ⟶	

(b)

Term number	Sequence
1 ⟶	5
2 ⟶	10
3 ⟶	15
⋮	⋮
10 ⟶	
⋮	⋮
100 ⟶	
⋮	⋮
n ⟶	

(c)

Term number	Sequence
1 ⟶	12
2 ⟶	24
3 ⟶	36
⋮	⋮
10 ⟶	
⋮	⋮
100 ⟶	
⋮	⋮
n ⟶	

(d)

Term number	Sequence
1 ⟶	−1
2 ⟶	0
3 ⟶	1
⋮	⋮
10 ⟶	
⋮	⋮
100 ⟶	
⋮	⋮
n ⟶	

(e)

Term number	Sequence
1 ⟶	2
2 ⟶	4
3 ⟶	6
⋮	⋮
10 ⟶	
⋮	⋮
100 ⟶	
⋮	⋮
n ⟶	

(f)

Term number	Sequence
1 ⟶	−1
2 ⟶	−2
3 ⟶	−3
⋮	⋮
10 ⟶	
⋮	⋮
100 ⟶	
⋮	⋮
n ⟶	

(g)

Term number	Sequence
1 ——→	100
2 ——→	200
3 ——→	300
⋮	⋮
10 ——→	
⋮	⋮
100 ——→	
⋮	⋮
n ——→	

(h)

Term number	Sequence
1 ——→	30
2 ——→	60
3 ——→	90
⋮	⋮
10 ——→	
⋮	⋮
100 ——→	
⋮	⋮
n ——→	

(i)

Term number	Sequence
1 ——→	−3
2 ——→	−6
3 ——→	−9
⋮	⋮
10 ——→	
⋮	⋮
100 ——→	
⋮	⋮
n ——→	

2 For each of the sequences in question **1** compare the difference with the general rule. What do you notice?

■ **The difference between consecutive terms can help to find the first part of the general rule.**

Example 6

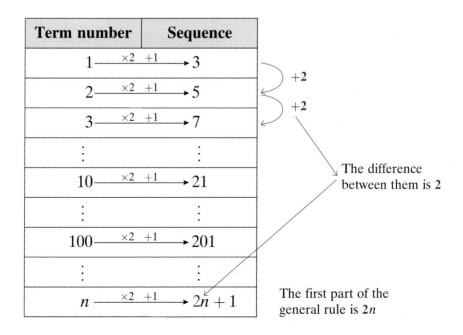

Term number	Sequence
1 —×2 +1→ 3	
2 —×2 +1→ 5	
3 —×2 +1→ 7	
⋮	⋮
10 —×2 +1→ 21	
⋮	⋮
100 —×2 +1→ 201	
⋮	⋮
n —×2 +1→ $2n + 1$	

+2
+2

The difference between them is **2**

The first part of the general rule is **2*n***

Exercise 9F

1 These sequences have been generated by two-step machines. For each one find the missing term and the general rule.
The first one has been done for you.

Hint: × and − Hint: × and +

(a)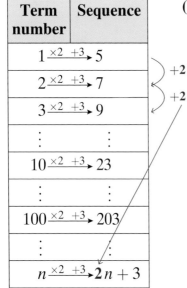

(b)

Term number	Sequence
1	1
2	3
3	5
⋮	⋮
10	
⋮	⋮
100	
⋮	⋮
n	

(c)

Term number	Sequence
1	7
2	11
3	15
⋮	⋮
10	
⋮	⋮
100	
⋮	⋮
n	

Hint: × and − Hint: × and − Hint: × and +

(d)

Term number	Sequence
1	−1
2	1
3	3
⋮	⋮
10	
⋮	⋮
100	
⋮	⋮
n	

(e)

Term number	Sequence
1	−3
2	−5
3	−7
⋮	⋮
10	
⋮	⋮
100	
⋮	⋮
n	

(f)

Term number	Sequence
1	4
2	1
3	−2
⋮	⋮
10	
⋮	⋮
100	
⋮	⋮
n	

(g)

Term number	Sequence
1	2
2	11
3	20
⋮	⋮
10	
⋮	⋮
100	
⋮	⋮
n	

(h)

Term number	Sequence
1	100
2	98
3	96
⋮	⋮
10	
⋮	⋮
100	
⋮	⋮
n	

(i)

Term number	Sequence
1	30
2	41
3	52
⋮	⋮
10	
⋮	⋮
100	
⋮	⋮
n	

2 For each of these sequences find
- the general term
- the 12th term
- the 100th term

(a) 7, 14, 21, 28, ... (b) 1, 5, 9, 13, ...
(c) 6, 9, 12, 15, ... (d) 13, 26, 39, 52, ...
(e) 0, 1, 2, 3, ... (f) 5, 4, 3, 2, ...
(g) −5, −4, −3, −2, ... (h) 9, 14, 19, 24, ...

Summary of key points

1 When exploring number sequences you can find:
- a rule to find the next term
- a rule to find the nth term.

2 The nth term rule is also called the **general rule**.

3 To help find the general rule write the term numbers and sequence in a table.

4 The difference between consecutive terms can help to find the first part of the general rule.

10 Working with algebra

To solve problems using algebra you need to be able to manipulate symbols and numbers in algebra with confidence.

10.1 Remember terms and expressions

- **In algebra a collection of letters and numbers is called a term,**

  e.g. $3x$ is a term in x

  $5xy$ is a term in x and y

- **A collection of terms is called an expression,**

  e.g. $4x + 7y$ is an algebraic expression which has two terms, $4x$ and $7y$

- **In algebra terms that contain exactly the same letters are called like terms,**

  e.g. $2x$ and $5x$ are like terms because they both contain only x.

- **You can make expressions simpler by combining like terms,**

  e.g. $3x + x - 2x = 4x - 2x = 2x$

Example 1

Simplify $3x + 7x - 4x$

These are all terms in x

So work out $3 + 7 - 4 = 6$

Then $3x + 7x - 4x = 6x$

Exercise 10A

Simplify:

1 $3x + 5x$

2 $6y - 2y$

3 $5x + 8x + x$

4 $7a + 3a - 4a$

5 $11t + 5t - 15t + 3t$

6 $2y - 7y - 5y + 3y$

7 $2x + 3y + 5x + 4y$

8 $3a + 5b + 6a + 7b$

9 $3r + 5t - 2r + t$

10 $8x - 5y - 10x + 2y$

11 $3m - 5 + 2m + 7$

12 $9f + 2g - 5g + 4f$

13 $11 + 2p + 7 - 5p$

14 $1 + 2x + 3y + 7x + 8y$

15 $7a - b + a + b - 2$

16 $15a + 2b + 14a - 3b$

17 $1 - x + 2y + x - 2y$

18 $7x + 8x + 9 + 3x - 2$

19 $16g + 2h - 6h - 4h + g$

20 $11p - 15q + 2p - 2q$

21 $6x + 2y - 10x + 7y$

22 $5m - 6n + 8m - 6n$

23 $d + 3a + d - 4a - d$

24 $4a + 3b - 2 + 3b - a$

25 $x - 7y + 2x + 7y + 3x$

26 $16p + 9r - 7p + 4r + 3p$

10.2 Powers in algebra

Powers are used in algebra to help write terms in a shorter form.

$y \times y = y^2$ y squared or y to the power of 2

$y \times y \times y = y^3$ y cubed or y to the power of 3

$y \times y \times y \times y = y^4$ y to the power of 4

Another word for power is **index**.

■ y^x **means y to the power of x.**
x is called the power or index.
e.g. $y^6 = y \times y \times y \times y \times y \times y$

Notice that $y^1 = y$.

Example 2

Write $4 \times 4 \times 4$ using powers.

There are 3 lots of 4 multiplied together

So $4 \times 4 \times 4 = 4^3$

Example 3

Write $a \times a \times a \times a \times a$ using powers.

There are 5 lots of a multiplied together

So $a \times a \times a \times a \times a = a^5$

Example 4

Write r^4 without powers.

r^4 means 4 lots of r multiplied together

So $r^4 = r \times r \times r \times r$

Exercise 10B

1 Write the following using powers:

(a) $5 \times 5 \times 5$ (b) $y \times y \times y \times y$

(c) $r \times r$ (d) $3 \times 3 \times 3 \times 3 \times 3$

(e) $b \times b \times b$ (f) 7×7

(g) $a \times a \times a \times a \times a$ (h) $d \times d \times d$

(i) $e \times e \times e \times e \times e \times e$ (j) $f \times f \times f \times f$

(k) $t \times t \times t \times t$ (l) $w \times w \times w \times w \times w \times w \times w$

2 Write without powers:

(a) 2^3 (b) 5^2 (c) 4^5

(d) x^3 (e) y^4 (f) t^2

(g) w^5 (h) m^4 (i) v^6

(j) b^7 (k) e^3 (l) q^6

(m) p^5 (n) c^9

10.3 Multiplying powers of the same number or letter

You need to be able to multiply powers of the same number together.

$$y^2 \times y^3 = (y \times y) \times (y \times y \times y) = y^5$$

$$y^2 \times y^3 = y^{2+3} = y^5$$

> In total you are multiplying together $2 + 3 = 5$ lots of y.

■ **To multiply powers of numbers or letters add the powers together:**

$$x^a \times x^b = x^{a+b}$$

Example 5

Simplify   (a) $x^5 \times x^3$ (b) $y^6 \times y$

(a) $x^5 \times x^3 = x^{5+3} = x^8$

(b) $y^6 \times y = y^{6+1} = y^7$

Example 6

Simplify $3x^2 \times 2x^5$

$3x^2 \times 2x^5$ means $3 \times x^2 \times 2 \times x^5$

Multiply the numbers together and multiply the terms in x together:

$$3 \times 2 \times x^2 \times x^5$$
$$= 6 \times x^{2+5}$$
$$= 6x^7$$

Exercise 10C

Simplify:

1 $x^2 \times x^3$ **2** $y^4 \times y^3$ **3** $a \times a^5$

4 $y^4 \times y^3$ **5** $x^5 \times x^4$ **6** $b^2 \times b^3 \times b$

7 $t^4 \times t^2 \times t^3$ **8** $y^2 \times y^4 \times y^5$ **9** $x \times x \times x^4$

10 $m^3 \times m^4 \times m^5$ **11** $2x \times 3x^2$ **12** $2y^3 \times 5y^2$

13 $5a^2 \times 10a^5$ **14** $3b^2 \times 5b^4$ **15** $3x^4 \times 4x^5$

16 $4d^7 \times 3d^2$ **17** $10a^2 \times 9a^5$ **18** $3x^4 \times 4x^5$

19 $8d^3 \times 3d^4$ **20** $6x^3 \times 7x^4$ **21** $2a^2 \times 2a^2$

22 $y^2 \times y^2 \times y^2$ **23** $4y^3 \times 2y^2 \times y$ **24** $3x^2 \times 2x^2 \times 6$

25 $3a^2 \times 2a^3 \times 5a^2$

10.4 Expanding brackets in algebra

Sometimes algebraic expressions have brackets

$3(a + b)$ means 3 lots of $a + b$

or $a + b + a + b + a + b$

Collecting like terms:

$$3(a + b) = 3a + 3b$$

So each term inside the brackets has been multiplied by 3.

■ **To expand brackets multiply each term inside the brackets by the term outside the brackets.**

Writing an expression without brackets is called **expanding the brackets** or **multiplying out the brackets**.

Example 7

Expand $3(5a - 2b)$.

Multiply each term inside the brackets by 3:
$$3(5a - 2b) = 3 \times 5a - 3 \times 2b$$
$$= 15a - 6b$$

Example 8

Write $2x(3 + y)$ without brackets.

Multiply each term inside the bracket by $2x$:
$$2x(3 + y) = 2x \times 3 + 2x \times y$$
$$= 6x + 2xy$$

Example 9

Expand $3y(y - x)$.

Multiply each term inside the bracket by $3y$:
$$3y(y - x) = 3y \times y - 3y \times x$$
$$= 3y^2 - 3xy$$

Remember:
$$y \times y = y^1 \times y^1 = y^{1+1} = y^2$$

Exercise 10D

1 Expand the brackets in these expressions:

(a) $2(2x + 5y)$ (b) $4(3x - 2y)$ (c) $3(5x + 8y)$

(d) $2(3x + 9y)$ (e) $5(4x - 5y)$ (f) $6(7x - 2y)$

2 Write these expressions without brackets:

(a) $3x(2x + 1)$ (b) $2y(3y - 8)$ (c) $4a(2 - 5a)$

(d) $3m(7 + m)$ (e) $5p(3p + 7)$ (f) $7s(s^2 + 2)$

3 Expand the brackets in these expressions:

(**a**) $3x(5 + 2y)$ (**b**) $4p(w + 3z)$ (**c**) $7p(3s - 1)$

(**d**) $5y(2y - 1)$ (**e**) $4a(7 - 3b)$ (**f**) $11m(4m - 5)$

4 Expand the brackets in these expressions:

(**a**) $a(4a - 3)$ (**b**) $2x(3x - 2y)$ (**c**) $4(x - 5)$

(**d**) $y(y + x)$ (**e**) $4x^3(x^2 - 2)$ (**f**) $5x(3x^2 - 4x^3)$

10.5 Adding expressions with brackets

You will need to be able to add expressions containing brackets.

For example $2(2y + x) + 3(y + 3x)$

■ **To simplify expressions containing brackets:**
  - **expand the brackets**
  - **collect like terms**

Example 10

Expand the brackets in this expression and then collect like terms.

$$2(2y + x) + 3(y + 3x)$$

Expand the brackets: $4y + 2x + 3y + 9x$

Collect like terms: $4y + 3y + 2x + 9x$

$$7y \ + \ 11x$$

$$2(2y + x) + 3(y + 3x) = 7y + 11x$$

Example 11

Simplify $3(2y + 5x) + 4(y - 2x)$

$$6y + 15x + 4y - 8x$$

$$6y + 4y + 15x - 8x$$

$$10y \ + \ 7x$$

$$3(2y + 5x) + 4(y - 2x) = 10y + 7x$$

Exercise 10E

1 Expand the brackets in these expressions and then collect like terms.

(a) $3(y + x) + 2(y + x)$ (b) $4(b + a) + 3(b + a)$

(c) $2(3y + x) + 2(2y + 3x)$ (d) $3(2b + a) + 4(b + a)$

(e) $3(4b + 3a) + 2(2b - 3c)$ (f) $4(p + q) + 2(2q - p)$

(g) $3(3d + 2c) + 5(d - c)$ (h) $5(q + p) + 6(2q + 3p)$

(i) $5(y - 2x) + 3(2y + 5x)$ (j) $3(4t - 5s) + 7(2t + 3s)$

2 Simplify:

(a) $3(y - x) + 3(y + x)$ (b) $2(3b + 4a) + 3(2b - 3a)$

(c) $8(3y - 2x) + 4(7y - 3x)$ (d) $4(3y - 2x) + 3(y - x)$

(e) $2(y + 3x) + 7(4y + 3x)$ (f) $7(3a + 5b) + 4(5a + 3b)$

(g) $5(2p + q) + 2(p - 3q)$ (h) $3(3y - 2x) + 4(2y - x)$

(i) $9(2b + a) + 2(b - 4a)$ (j) $4(e + 2g) + 3(e - g)$

10.6 Subtracting expressions with brackets

You can use the same method to subtract expressions containing brackets.

Example 12

Expand the brackets in this expression and then collect like terms.

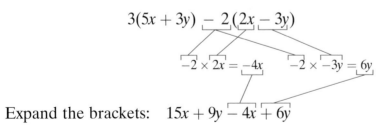

$$3(5x + 3y) - 2(2x - 3y)$$

$$-2 \times 2x = -4x \qquad -2 \times -3y = 6y$$

Expand the brackets: $15x + 9y - 4x + 6y$

Collect like terms: $11x + 15y$

$$3(5x + 3y) - 2(2x - 3y) = 11x + 15y$$

Example 13

Simplify $3(4x + 3y) - 2(2x - y)$.

Expand the brackets:
$$3(4x + 3y) - 2(2x - y)$$
$$= 3 \times 4x + 3 \times 3y - 2 \times 2x - 2 \times -y$$
$$= 12x + 9y - 4x + 2y$$

Collect like terms:
$$12x - 4x + 9y + 2y$$
$$= 8x + 11y$$

Example 14

Simplify $5(2x - 3y) - (x + 3y)$.

Expand the brackets: $\quad 10x - 15y - x - 3y$

Collect like terms: $\quad 10x - x - 15y - 3y$
$$= 9x - 18y$$

Remember:
$-(x + 3y)$ means $-1(x + 3y)$

Example 15

Simplify $t^2(t^3 - 6) + t^2(t^3 + 5)$.

Expand the brackets:
$$t^2(t^3 - 6) + t^2(t^3 + 5)$$
$$= t^{2+3} - 6t^2 + t^{2+3} + 5t^2$$
$$= t^5 - 6t^2 + t^5 + 5t^2$$

Collect like terms:
$$t^5 + t^5 - 6t^2 + 5t^2$$
$$= 2t^5 - t^2$$

Exercise 10F

Simplify these expressions:

1 $2(2x + y) - 3(x + 2y)$
2 $5(2x + 3y) - 2(2x + 3y)$
3 $3(4x - 3y) - (2x + y)$
4 $2(x + y) - 2(x - y)$
5 $5(3a + 2b) - 3(a - b)$
6 $4(2x + y) - 5(x + 2y)$
7 $4(2x + 3y) - 5(x - 2y)$
8 $7(3a - b) - (2a - 5b)$
9 $3(4a - 5b) - 2(3a + 2b)$
10 $3(7x - y) - 2(x + 5y)$
11 $2(7x + y) - 3(5x - 2y)$
12 $4(3a - b) - 3(2a + 3b)$

13 $4(a - 6b) - (3a - 2b)$

14 $3(3x - 2y) - 2(3x + 2y)$

15 $5(3n - 2m) - 7(n - m)$

16 $5(r + 3t) - 3(2r - 3t)$

17 $4(a + 2b) - 4(2a - b)$

18 $6(3a + 2b) - 5(2a - 3b)$

19 $2(2x + 3y) - 7(3x - 5y)$

20 $3(2x + y) - 2(x + y) - (2x - y)$

21 $y(2x + y^2) - 3x(4x^2 + y^2)$

22 $4w(w + 3x) - 4w^2(3w^3 + 5xw)$

23 $2t^3(6t^2 + 3) - t^3(3t^2 - 5)$

24 $5x^2(3x^3 - 2x) - 2x^3(3x^2 - 1)$

10.7 Factorising simple expressions

 Factorising is the reverse process to removing brackets.

Factorising lets you write algebraic expressions in a different form using brackets.

Example 16

Factorise the expression $4x + 8$.

Look for common factors of the terms $4x$ and 8.

4 is a common factor (because 4 goes into 4 and 8 exactly) so 4 can be put outside a bracket:

$$4x + 8 = 4(x + 2)$$

You can check your answers by expanding the brackets:
$$4(x + 2) = 4 \times x + 4 \times 2$$
$$= 4x + 8$$

Example 17

Factorise $12y - 18x$.

Look for common factors of the terms $12y$ and $18x$.

6 is a common factor because it goes into 12 and 18 exactly so it can be placed outside the brackets:

$$12y - 18x = 6(2y - 3x)$$

Example 18

Factorise $8a + 4$.

Look for common factors of the terms $8a$ and 4.

4 is a common factor so it can be placed outside brackets:

$$4(2a + 1)$$

Exercise 10G

Factorise each of these expressions:

1 $2x + 4y$ **2** $3y + 9z$ **3** $15a + 3$ **4** $18d - 6$

5 $7w + 21y$ **6** $15 - 25x$ **7** $12a - 20$ **8** $6b - 3c$

9 $16 + 24x$ **10** $9a + 15b$ **11** $11c - 77$ **12** $60a + 12b$

13 $9x + 15y$ **14** $6a - 9b$ **15** $3x - 6y$ **16** $75a + 15b$

10.8 Rearranging a formula

Here is part of a sequence of shapes made from matchsticks.

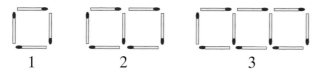

The first shape uses four matches. The second shape uses seven matches.

The nth shape uses $3n + 1$ matches.

If the total number of matches used in each shape is T, you write:

$$T = 3n + 1$$

You need to use your formula to find which number shape you can make from a certain number of matches.

Here is the flowchart for the formula:

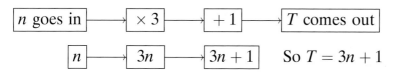

Here is the inverse flowchart:

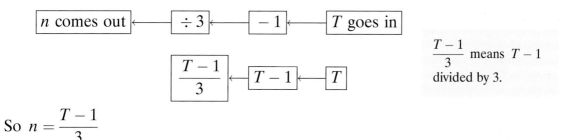

$\dfrac{T - 1}{3}$ means $T - 1$ divided by 3.

So $n = \dfrac{T - 1}{3}$

Changing the formula $T = 3n + 1$ so that it becomes $n = \dfrac{T - 1}{3}$ is called rearranging the formula to make n the subject.

■   **The subject of a formula appears on its own on one side of the formula and does not appear on the other side.**

Example 19

Leonie uses 43 matchsticks to make a pattern of matchsticks like the ones on page 169.

Work out which number shape he makes using the formula $n = \dfrac{T - 1}{3}$.

Here $T = 43$

So put $T = 43$ into $n = \dfrac{T - 1}{3}$ to find the shape number.

$$n = \frac{43 - 1}{3}$$
$$= \frac{42}{3}$$
$$= 14$$

So using 43 matchsticks makes the 14th shape.

You can rearrange formulae yourself using two methods.

Example 20

Rearrange the formula $y = \dfrac{x}{3} - 7$ to make x the subject.

Flowchart method
Write the flowchart for the formula:

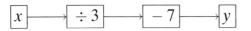

Write the inverse flowchart:

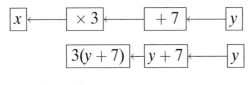

So $x = 3(y + 7)$

Balancing method

$$y = \frac{x}{3} - 7$$

Remember: Always do the same thing to both sides of the equation.

Add 7 to both sides

$$y + 7 = \frac{x}{3} - 7 + 7$$

$$y + 7 = \frac{x}{3}$$

Multiply both sides by 3. Use brackets around $y + 7$ because it all needs to be multiplied by 3.

$$3(y + 7) = \cancel{3} \times \frac{x}{\cancel{3}}$$

the threes will *cancel* each other out

$$3(y + 7) = x$$

So $x = 3y + 21$

Exercise 10H

1 The formula for the number of cards c in a card house of height h is:

$$c = 3h + 2$$

(a) Draw the flowchart for the formula $c = 3h + 2$

(b) (i) Draw the inverse flowchart to make h the subject of the formula.

(ii) Use the inverse flowchart to make h the subject.

(c) Use your formula to work out the height of card house that can be made with 41 cards.

2 Rearrange each of these formulae to make x the subject:

(a) $y = 2x + 3$ (b) $y = 5x + 2$ (c) $y = 2(x + 3)$

(d) $y = 3(x - 4)$ (e) $y = \frac{x}{3} - 4$ (f) $y = \frac{x + 3}{2}$

(g) $y = \frac{2x + 3}{6}$ (h) $y = \frac{x - 12}{7}$ (i) $y = \frac{x}{4} + 9$

(j) $y = 3(2x - 5)$ (k) $y = \frac{3x - 4}{2}$ (l) $y = 2(x + 3) + 5(x - 1)$

Summary of key points

1 In algebra a collection of letters and numbers is called a term,

 e.g. $3x$ is a term in x

  $5xy$ is a term in x and y

2 A collection of terms is called an expression,

 e.g. $4x + 7y$ is an algebraic expression which has two terms, $4x$ and $4y$

3 In algebra terms that contain exactly the same letters are called like terms,

 e.g. $2x$ and $5x$ are like terms because they both contain only x.

4 You can make expressions simpler by combining like terms,

 e.g. $3x + x - 2x = 4x - 2x = 2x$

5 y^x means y to the power of x.

 x is called the power or index.

 e.g. $y^6 = y \times y \times y \times y \times y \times y$

6 To multiply powers of numbers or letters add the powers together:

  $x^a \times x^b = x^{a+b}$

7 To expand brackets multiply each term inside the brackets by the term outside the brackets.

8 To simplify expressions containing brackets:
 • expand the brackets
 • collect like terms

9 Factorising is the reverse process to removing brackets.

10 The subject of a formula appears on its own on one side of the formula and does not appear on the other side.

11 Transformations

11.1 Different types of transformations

Reflections, rotations and translations are all called
transformations.

1 Copy each shape accurately and draw all the possible
   lines of reflection.

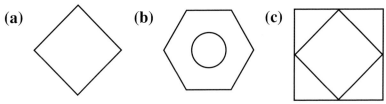

  (a)   (b)   (c)

2 Copy and complete the shapes by using the dotted line
   as the line of reflection.

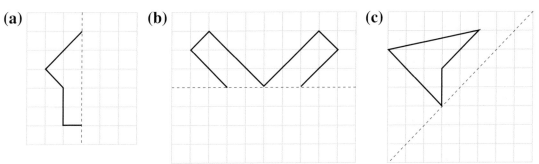

  (a)   (b)   (c)

3 Copy and complete the following rotations using the
   marked point as the centre of rotation.

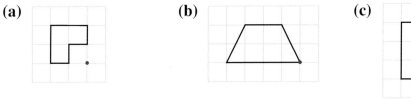

  (a)   (b)   (c)

    90° clockwise   90° anticlockwise   half turn (180°)

4 Copy and translate this shape
by 5 units in the *x* direction
and 2 units in the *y* direction.

Now translate the new image by
2 units in the *x* direction
and −4 units in the *y* direction.

11.2 Two-way mirror lines

■ **Mirror lines work in both directions as they are lines
of reflection.**

Example 1

Complete the diagram using the dotted line as the line of reflection.

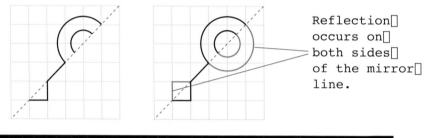

```
Reflection
occurs on
both sides
of the mirror
line.
```

Exercise 11B

In each question copy and complete the diagram using the
dotted lines as lines of reflection.

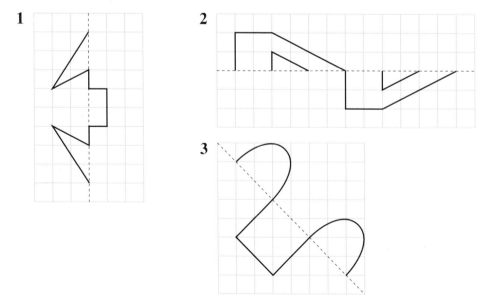

4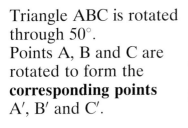

5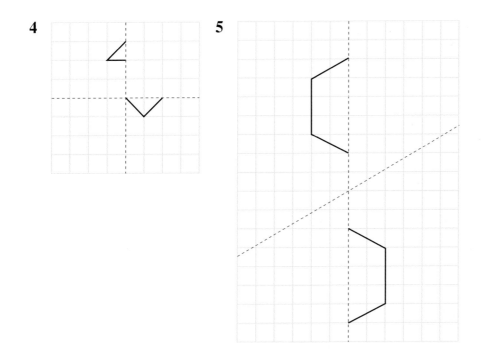

11.3 Finding the centre of rotation

Triangle ABC is rotated through 50°.
Points A, B and C are rotated to form the **corresponding points** A′, B′ and C′.

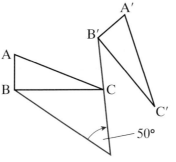

Join up any two pairs of corresponding points (e.g. A-A′ and C-C′) and draw in their perpendicular bisectors:

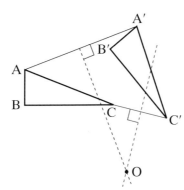

A **perpendicular bisector** to a line bisects it at right angles:

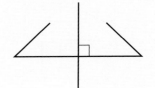

Bisect means 'cut exactly in half'.

■ **When a shape is rotated, the point where the perpendicular bisectors of corresponding points cross is called the centre of rotation.**

Example 2

ABCD is rotated to form A'B'C'D'.
Find the centre of rotation.

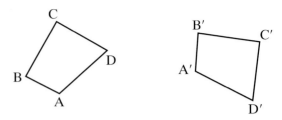

Connect up two pairs of corresponding points...

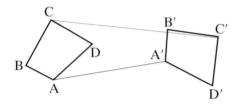

...and draw in the perpendicular bisectors

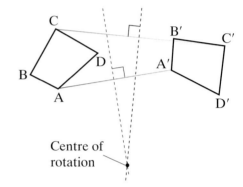

Centre of rotation

The point where the bisectors cross is the centre of rotation.

Exercise 11C

Copy the diagrams onto grid paper and find:
- the centre of rotation (you can check your answers by using tracing paper)
- the angle of the rotation.

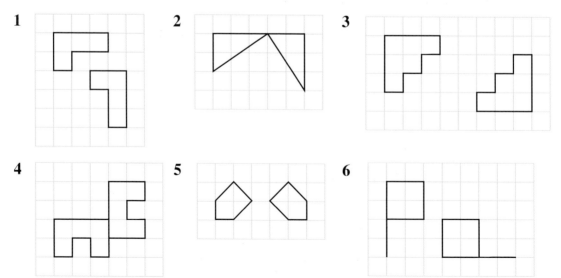

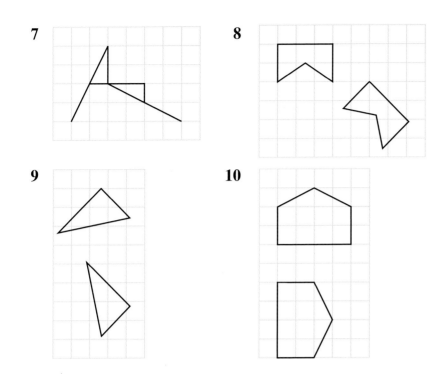

11.4 Enlargement

When a shape is enlarged all
the lengths are multiplied by
the same number and all the
angles stay the same.

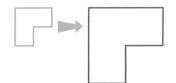

Enlargement by
scale factor 2

The number you multiply the lengths by to produce the
enlargement is called the scale factor (S.F.)

■ **The scale factor tells you what to multiply each length
by in an enlargement.**

Example 2

Draw an enlargement of this
shape of scale factor 3.

All the lengths need to be multiplied by 3:

$2 \times 3 = 6$

$5 \times 3 = 15$

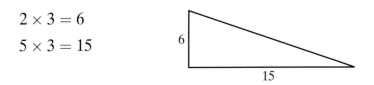

Exercise 11D

1 Copy each diagram and draw the enlargement by the stated scale factor.

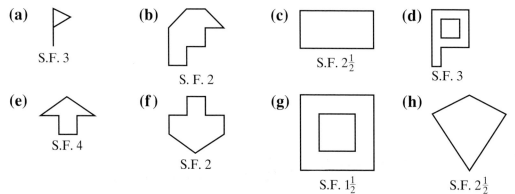

(a) S.F. 3

(b) S. F. 2

(c) S.F. $2\frac{1}{2}$

(d) S.F. 3

(e) S.F. 4

(f) S.F. 2

(g) S.F. $1\frac{1}{2}$

(h) S.F. $2\frac{1}{2}$

2 Find the scale factor of each enlargement.

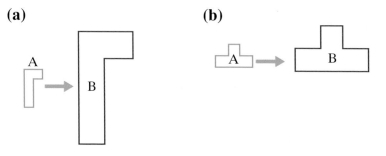

(a)

(b)

11.5 Centre of enlargement

Shapes are usually enlarged from a point known as the **centre of enlargement**.

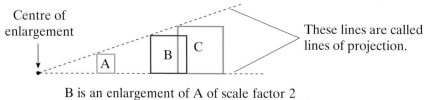

Centre of enlargement

These lines are called lines of projection.

B is an enlargement of A of scale factor 2
C is an enlargement of A of scale factor 2.5

A, B and C all have the same centre of enlargement.
The lines of projection help you to draw the enlarged shape in the correct position.

■ **The centre of enlargement determines the final position of the enlarged shape.**

Example 4

Enlarge this triangle by a scale factor of 2:

(a) from the centre of enlargement point P

(b) from the centre of enlargement point Q.

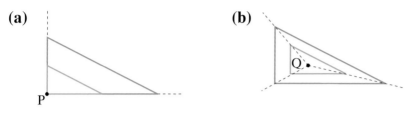

(a)   **(b)**

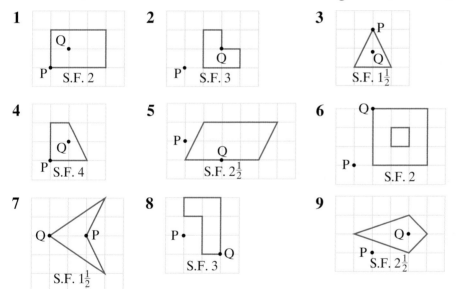

Exercise 11E

Copy each diagram and draw two enlargements by the stated
scale factor, one from each of the centres of enlargement, P and Q.

1 Q• P• S.F. 2

2 P• Q S.F. 3

3 P•Q S.F. $1\frac{1}{2}$

4 Q• P• S.F. 4

5 P• Q S.F. $2\frac{1}{2}$

6 Q• P• S.F. 2

7 Q• •P S.F. $1\frac{1}{2}$

8 P• •Q S.F. 3

9 P• Q• S.F. $2\frac{1}{2}$

11.6 Finding centres of enlargement and scale factors

Example 5

Shape A has been enlarged to
become shape B.
Find the centre and the scale factor
of the enlargement.

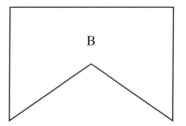

Draw lines joining at least two corresponding vertices.
Extend the lines until they cross at a point: this point is the
centre of enlargement.

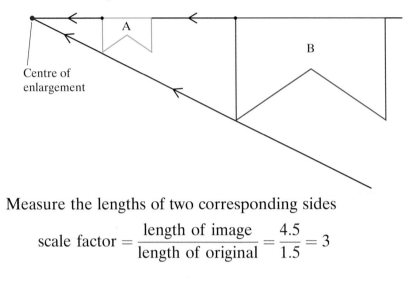

Measure the lengths of two corresponding sides

$$\text{scale factor} = \frac{\text{length of image}}{\text{length of original}} = \frac{4.5}{1.5} = 3$$

Exercise 11F

Each diagrams shows a shape A and its enlarged shape B.
Copy each diagram. For each enlargement find

(a) the centre of enlargement

(b) the scale factor of the enlargement.

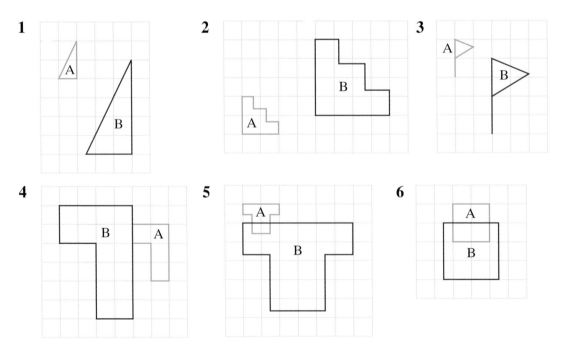

Summary of key points

1 Mirror lines work in both directions as they are lines of reflection.

2 When a shape is rotated, the point where the perpendicular bisectors of corresponding points cross is called the centre of rotation.

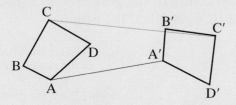

3 The scale factor tells you what to multiply each length by in an enlargement.

4 The centre of enlargement determines the final position of the enlarged shape.

12 Graphs

12.1 Coordinate grids

This coordinate grid shows part of the moon's surface.
The lunar lander is positioned at the centre of the grid.
It has coordinates (0, 0). The point (0, 0) is called the **origin**.

Remember:
Always go across
first ⟷
then up or down ↕

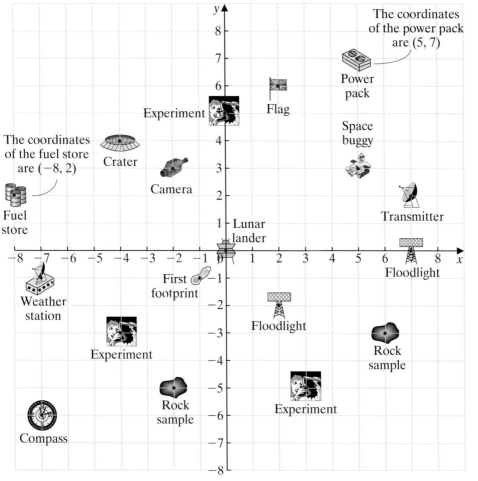

The coordinates
of the power pack
are (5, 7)

The coordinates
of the fuel store
are (−8, 2)

- The horizontal coordinate is called the *x*-coordinate.
- The vertical coordinate is called the *y*-coordinate.
- You always write the *x*-coordinate first.
- Each quarter of the coordinate grid is called a quadrant.

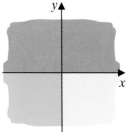

Exercise 12A

1 What are the coordinates of:

   (a) rock sample (2 answers) **(b)** space buggy **(c)** experiment (3 answers)

   (d) camera   **(e)** flag   **(f)** crater

2 What can be found at:

   (a) $(-7, -1)$ **(b)** $(7, 2)$ **(c)** $(2, -2)$

   (d) $(7, 0)$ **(e)** $(-7, -6)$ **(f)** $(-1, -1)$

3 The shapes on this grid are incomplete. For each shape write down the coordinates of the points given and the coordinates of the point needed to complete the shape.

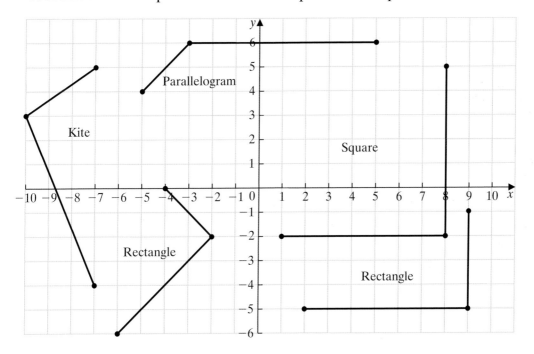

4 Draw a coordinate grid from -8 to 8 on both axes. Plot each set of points and join them in order: **Axes** is the plural of axis.

   (a) $(2, 7)$, $(8, 7)$, $(8, 1)$, $(2, 7)$

   (b) $(5, -1)$, $(7, -3)$, $(3, -7)$, $(1, -5)$, $(5, -1)$

   (c) $(3, 0)$, $(0, 3)$, $(-3, 0)$, $(0, -3)$, $(3, 0)$

   (d) $(-1, -3)$, $(-6, -3)$, $(-8, -6)$, $(-3, -6)$, $(-1, -3)$

   (e) $(-6, 0)$, $(-4, 0)$, $(-4, 2)$, $(-2, 2)$, $(-2, 4)$, $(-4, 4)$, $(-4, 6)$, $(-6, 6)$, $(-6, 4)$, $(-8, 4)$, $(-8, 2)$, $(-6, 2)$, $(-6, 0)$

   Name each of the shapes you have drawn.

5 Draw a coordinate grid from −8 to 8 on each axis.

   (a) Plot the following points and join them in order:
   (−6, −6), (−4, −2), (−8, 0), (−4, 2), (−6, 6),
   (−2, 4), (0, 8), (2, 4), (6, 6), (4, 2)

   (b) Can you see what is happening? Plot 7 more points
   and join them up to complete the shape. Write
   down the coordinates of the points you plotted.

12.2 Using fractions in coordinates

Sometimes objects are placed in positions that do not have
whole number coordinates. This coordinate grid shows the
layout of a holiday camp.

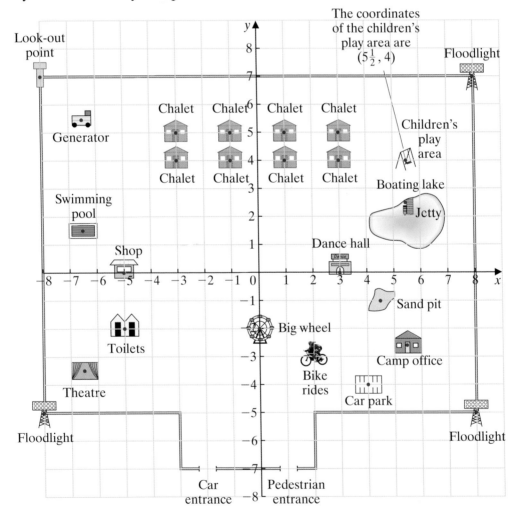

The *x*-coordinate of the children's play area is half way
between 5 and 6. It has *x*-coordinate $5\frac{1}{2}$.

Exercise 12B

1 Give the coordinates of the following:

   (a) jetty on the boating lake

   (b) camp office

   (c) pedestrian entry

   (d) floodlight (3 answers)

   (e) look-out point

   (f) theatre

   (g) shop

   (h) car park

2 What can be found at:

   (a) $(-3, 5)$ **(b)** $(1, 4)$

   (c) $(2, -3)$ **(d)** $(0, -2)$

   (e) $(-6\frac{1}{2}, 1\frac{1}{2})$ **(f)** $(3, 0)$

   (g) $(-6\frac{1}{2}, 5\frac{1}{2})$ **(h)** $(4\frac{1}{2}, -1)$

3 Draw a coordinate grid from -8 to 8.
Plot each set of points and join them in order.

   (a) $(0, -6)$, $(-1\frac{1}{2}, -3\frac{1}{2})$, $(-1\frac{1}{2}, 3\frac{1}{2})$, $(-\frac{1}{2}, 4\frac{1}{2})$, $(-1\frac{1}{2}, 5\frac{1}{2})$,
      $(-1\frac{1}{2}, 7\frac{1}{2})$, $(0, 8)$, $(1\frac{1}{2}, 7\frac{1}{2})$, $(1\frac{1}{2}, 5\frac{1}{2})$, $(\frac{1}{2}, 4\frac{1}{2})$, $(1\frac{1}{2}, 3\frac{1}{2})$,
      $(1\frac{1}{2}, -3\frac{1}{2})$, $(0, -6)$.

   (b) $(1\frac{1}{2}, 3\frac{1}{2})$, $(7, 8)$, $(7, 3)$, $(4, 0)$, $(6, 1)$, $(7, -5)$,
      $(1\frac{1}{2}, -3\frac{1}{2})$, $(1\frac{1}{2}, 3\frac{1}{2})$

   (c) $(-7, 8)$, $(-1\frac{1}{2}, 3\frac{1}{2})$, $(-1\frac{1}{2}, -3\frac{1}{2})$, $(-7, -5)$, $(-6, 1)$,
      $(-4, 0)$, $(-7, 3)$, $(-7, 8)$.

12.3 Lines on grids

Points on grids sometimes lie on straight lines.

You can label lines on grids using equations.

This grid shows the positions of motorcycles in a display team at the start of their display.

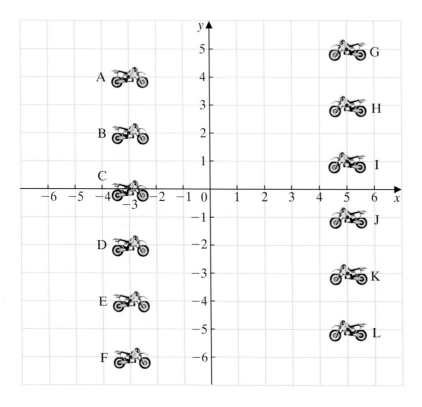

Motorcycles A, B, C, D, E and F are in a straight line.
Their coordinates are:

A(−3, 4)   B(−3, 2)   C(−3, 0)   D(−3, −2)   E(−3, −4)   F(−3, −6).

The x-coordinate of each point is −3.

The straight line the motorcycles are on is called $x = -3$.

$x = -3$ is the equation of the line.

Example 1

(a) Write down the coordinates of the motorcycles G, H, I, J, K and L.

(b) Find the equation of the straight line that the motorcycles are on.

(a) The coordinates are:

G(5, 5)   H(5, 3)   I(5, 1)   J(5, −1)   K(5, −3)   L(5, −5)

(b) The x-coordinate of each point is 5.
The equation of the line is $x = 5$.

Exercise 12C

1 These points are all on a
   straight line.

   (a) Write down the coordinates
       of each point.
   (b) Find the equation of
       the line.

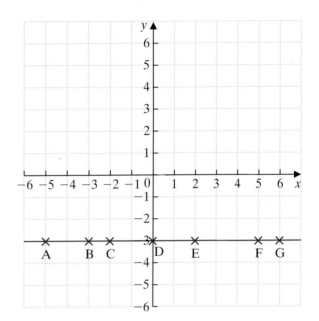

2 This grid shows the
   positions of the
   motorcycles half
   way through their
   display.

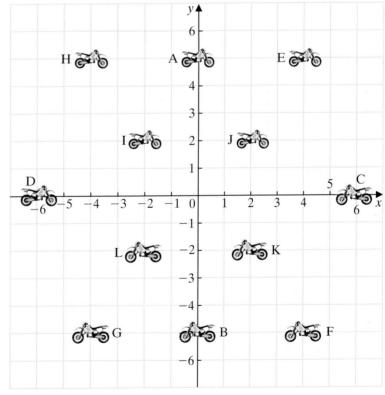

Find the equations of the straight lines joining the motorcycles:

(a) H, A and E   (b) H and G   (c) D and C   (d) A and B

(e) J and K   (f) L and K   (g) G, B and F   (h) E and F

3 Write down the equation of each line on this grid.

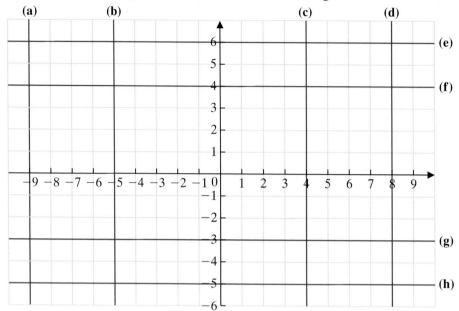

12.4 Drawing lines from equations

You can draw any straight line by finding two points on it.

Example 2

Draw the line with equation $y = 3$.

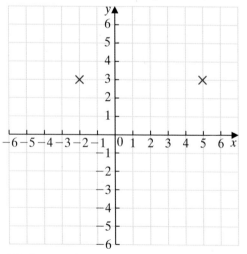

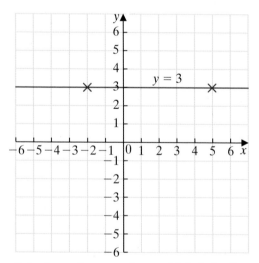

Find two points that will be on the line, for example $(-2, 3)$ and $(5, 3)$.

Join the points together and label the line.

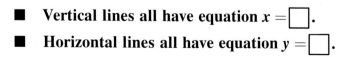

- **Vertical lines all have equation $x = \boxed{}$.**
- **Horizontal lines all have equation $y = \boxed{}$.**

Exercise 12D

1 Draw a coordinate grid from -6 to 6 on each axis.
Draw and label the lines with these equations:

(a) $x = 2$ (b) $y = -2$ (c) $x = -3$

(d) $y = 5$ (e) $x = 1$ (f) $y = -4$

2 Draw a coordinate grid from -6 to 6 on each axis.
For each set of equations:

- Draw and label the lines with those equations
- Shade in and name the shape produced.

(a) $x = 4, x = 2, y = -1, y = -3$.

(b) $x = -6, x = -3, y = 5, y = 3$.

12.5 Naming sloping lines

The points A, B, C and D are on a straight line. They have coordinates $(-6, 0)$, $(-4, 2)$, $(-2, 4)$ and $(0, 6)$.

To find the equation of the line, find a rule connecting the x-coordinate and the y-coordinate:

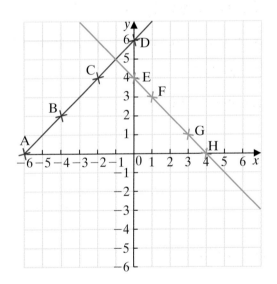

$$(-6, 0) \qquad (-4, 2) \qquad (-2, 4) \qquad (0, 6)$$
$$+6 \qquad\qquad +6 \qquad\qquad +6 \qquad\qquad +6$$

The rule to find the y-coordinate is 'add 6 to the x-coordinate'.
The equation of the line is $y = x + 6$.

Example 3

The points E, F, G and H are on a straight line.
Find the equation of the line.

Write down the coordinates of the points on the line:

$$(0, 4) \qquad (1, 3) \qquad (3, 1) \qquad (4, 0)$$
$$0 + 4 = 4 \quad 1 + 3 = 4 \quad 3 + 1 = 4 \quad 4 + 0 = 4$$

The rule is 'x-coordinate plus y-coordinate equals 4'.
The equation of the line is $x + y = 4$.

■ **To find the equation of a sloping line find a rule connecting the *x*-coordinate and the *y*-coordinate.**

● **If the line slopes diagonally upwards the equation will be $y = x + \square$ or $y = x - \square$.**

   e.g. $y = x + 6$

   $y = x - 2$

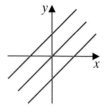

● **If the line slopes diagonally downwards the equation will be $x + y = \square$.**

   e.g. $x + y = 4$

   $x + y = -3$

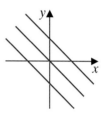

Exercise 12E

1 Find the equations of the lines on this grid:

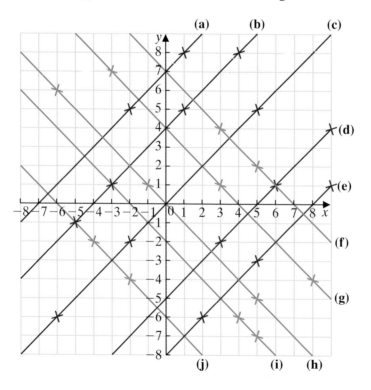

2 Find the equations of the lines on this grid:

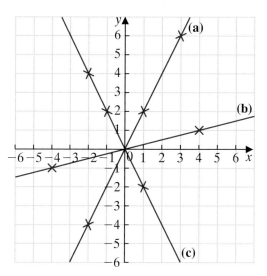

Remember: Write down the coordinates of the points on the line then look for a rule.

12.6 Drawing sloping lines

You can draw sloping lines using a table of values.

Example 4

Draw the line with equation $y = 2x + 1$.

Choose some values for x such as $-3, -2, -1, 0, 1, 2, 3$.

Draw a table like this:

x	-3	-2	-1	0	1	2	3
y							

Work out $2x + 1$ for each value of x.

For example, when

$$x = -1, y = 2 \times -1 + 1$$
$$= -2 + 1$$
$$= -1$$

x	-3	-2	-1	0	1	2	3
y	-5	-3	-1	1	3	5	7

Remember BIDMAS: You always multiply before you add.

The coordinates of the points on the line are:

(−3, −5)   (−2, −3)   (−1, −1)

(0, 1)   (1, 3)   (2, 5)   (3, 7)

Plot the points on a coordinate grid.
Draw and label the straight line.

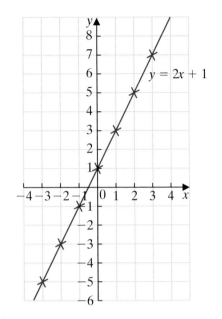

Exercise 12F

For each equation:

- copy and complete the table of values.
- plot the points on a coordinate grid and draw and label the line.

1 $y = x + 4$

x	−3	−2	−1	0	1	2	3
y			3				7

2 $y = x - 3$

x	−3	−2	−1	0	1	2	3
y	−6		−3				0

3 $y = 2x + 3$

x	−3	−2	−1	0	1	2	3
y			1			7	

4 $y = 3x - 2$

x	−3	−2	−1	0	1	2	3
y	−11				1		

5 $y = 5x + 3$

x	−3	−2	−1	0	1	2	3
y							

6 $y = 3x - 5$

x	−3	−2	−1	0	1	2	3
y							

7 $y = 5 - x$

x	−3	−2	−1	0	1	2	3
y							

8 $y = 1 - 2x$

x	−3	−2	−1	0	1	2	3
y							

12.7 Gradient and intercept

This grid shows the line with equation $y = 3x - 2$.
The line crosses the y-axis at the point $(0, -2)$.
This point is called the **intercept**.

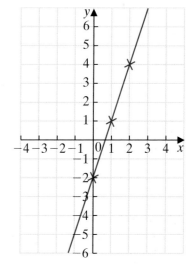

■ **The intercept of a line is the point $(0, \boxed{})$**
  where the line crosses the y-axis. The number
  in the box is the value of y when $x = 0$.

Example 5

Find the intercept of the line $y = 4x + 5$.

The intercept is the point $(0, \boxed{})$.
Put $x = 0$ into the equation.

$$y = 4 \times 0 + 5 = 0 + 5 = 5$$

The intercept is $(0, 5)$.

This cyclist is on a steep hill.
The steepness of the hill is called the gradient.
Steep hills have large gradients.
Shallow hills have small gradients.

■ **Gradient is the mathematical word for steepness.**
The bigger the gradient, the steeper the slope.

   ● **A line that slopes up has positive gradient.**

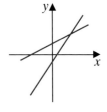

   ● **A line that slopes down has negative gradient.**

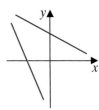

Example 6

Put these lines in order according to
their gradients, greatest first.

The order is **b, a, e, d, c.**

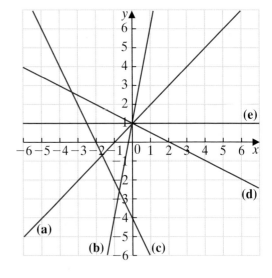

Exercise 12G

1 Find the intercept of each line:

   (a) $y = x + 3$ **(b)** $y = x - 2$ **(c)** $y = 2x + 5$ **(d)** $y = 3x + 1$

   (e) $y = x$ **(f)** $y = 4x$ **(g)** $y = 2 - x$ **(h)** $y = 3 - 2x$

   (i) $y = 3x - 4$ **(j)** $y = 2x - 5$ **(k)** $y = -x$ **(l)** $y = -3x + 1$

2 Put these lines in order according to their gradients, greatest first.

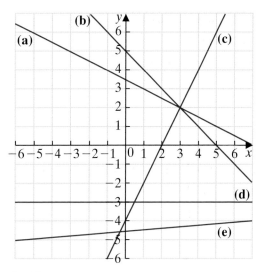

3 Draw a coordinate grid from -8 to 8 on both axes.

(a) Using tables of values draw and label each line:

(i) $y = 2x - 1$ (ii) $y = 2x + 2$
(iii) $y = 2x + 4$ (iv) $y = 2x - 3$

(b) Write down the intercept of each line.

(c) What can you say about the gradients of your four lines?

4 Draw a coordinate grid from -10 to 10 on both axes.

(a) Using tables of values draw and label each line:

(i) $y = x + 2$ (ii) $y = 2x + 2$
(iii) $y = 3x + 2$ (iv) $y = 4x + 2$

(b) Put the lines in order according to their gradients, greatest first.

(c) What can you say about the intercepts of your four lines?

5 Draw a coordinate grid from -10 to 10 on both axes.

(a) Using tables of values draw and label each line:

(i) $y = 2x$ (ii) $y = -2x$
(iii) $y = 3x$ (iv) $y = -3x$

(b) What do you notice about lines (i) and (ii), and lines (iii) and (iv)?

(c) Using a table of values draw and label the line $y = \frac{1}{2}x$.

(d) Using your answer to (b), and without using a table of values, draw and label the line $y = -\frac{1}{2}x$.

12.8 Equations of curves

You need to be able to draw the lines of more complicated equations.

Example 7

Draw the line with equation $y = x^2$.

Choose some values for x:
$-4, -3, -2, -1, 0, 1, 2, 3, 4$.

Work out y for each value of x.

For example when
$x = -3, y = (-3)^2 = -3 \times -3 = 9$.

Draw a table of values:

x	-4	-3	-2	-1	0	1	2	3	4
y	16	9	4	1	0	1	4	9	16

The coordinates of the points on the line are:

$(-4, 16)$ $(-3, 9)$ $(-2, 4)$ $(-1, 1)$
$(0, 0)$ $(1, 1)$ $(2, 4)$ $(3, 9)$ $(4, 16)$

The points are not in a straight line.

Join the points together with a **smooth curve** and label the line.

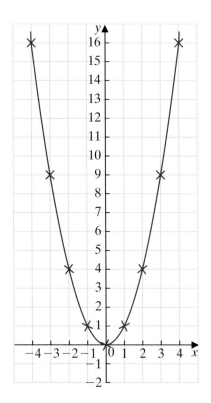

Exercise 12H

For each equation:

- copy and complete the table of values.
- plot the points on a coordinate grid and draw and label the line.

1 $y = x^2 + 1$

x	-3	-2	-1	0	1	2	3
y		5		1			

Hint: When drawing curves you might find it easier to turn the paper and draw a curve like this:

instead of like this:

2 $y = x^2 - 1$

x	−3	−2	−1	0	1	2	3
y		3					8

3 $y = 2x^2 + 1$

x	−3	−2	−1	0	1	2	3
y		9			3		

4 $y = 1 - x^2$

x	−3	−2	−1	0	1	2	3
y		−3				−3	

5 $y = 2x^2 + 3$

x	−3	−2	−1	0	1	2	3
y	21				5		

6 $y = x^2 + x$

x	−3	−2	−1	0	1	2	3
y		2				6	

7 $y = 3x^2 - 2x + 1$

x	−3	−2	−1	0	1	2	3
y	34					9	

8 $y = x^2 + 2x - 3$

x	−3	−2	−1	0	1	2	3
y							

12.9 Using graphs

When you draw the line $y = x^2$ on a coordinate grid,
you are drawing the **graph** of $y = x^2$.

■ **A graph shows a relationship on a coordinate grid.**

Example 8

Sam and Anna are testing a spring.
This graph shows the relationship
between the length of the spring
and the mass hung on it.

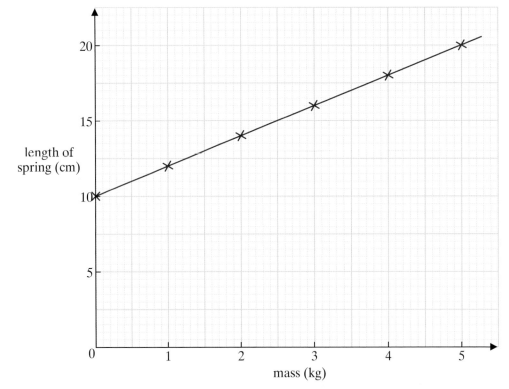

Use the graph to find:

(a) the length of the spring with no mass on it

(b) the length of the spring with a mass of 4.5 kg

(c) the mass needed to make the spring 13 cm long.

(a) When the mass is 0 kg, the spring is 10 cm long.

(b)

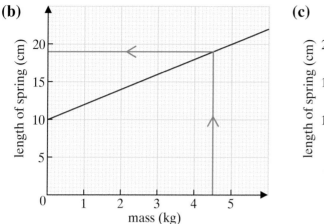

Read up from the 'mass' axis and across to the 'length' axis. The answer is 19 cm.

(c)

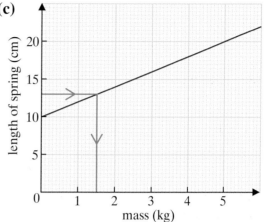

Read across from the 'length' axis and down to the 'mass' axis. The answer is 1.5 kg.

Using a scale

Graphs often have different scales on each axis. The most common scales are:

- the factors of 10: 1, 2, 5, 10

- the multiples of 10: 10, 20, 50, 100 …

You work out a scale like this:

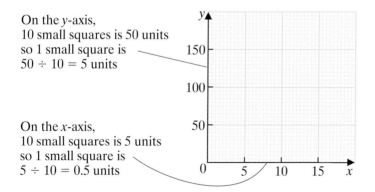

On the y-axis,
10 small squares is 50 units
so 1 small square is
$50 \div 10 = 5$ units

On the x-axis,
10 small squares is 5 units
so 1 small square is
$5 \div 10 = 0.5$ units

Always remember to count in the scale that you are using.

For example, if you use 10 small squares for 5 units, count in steps of 5: 5, 10, 15, …

If you use 10 small squares for 50 units, count in steps of 50: 50, 100, 150, 200, …

Exercise 12I

1 This graph can be used to convert British pounds (£) to Spanish pesetas (ptas).

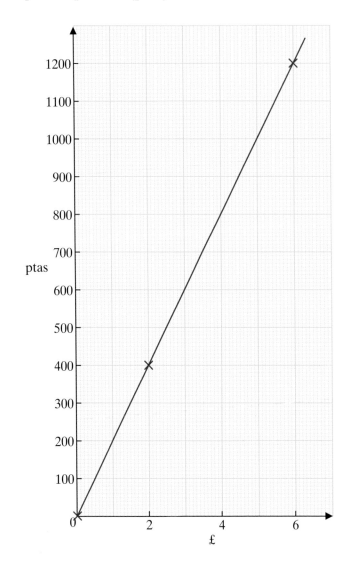

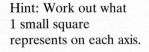

Hint: Work out what 1 small square represents on each axis.

Use the graph to change these amounts into pesetas:

(a) £3   (b) £5

(c) £2.50   (d) £1.50

Change these amounts into pounds:

(e) 500 ptas   (f) 800 ptas

(g) 600 ptas   (h) 350 ptas

2 This graph shows how the cost of a taxi ride depends
on the length of the journey.

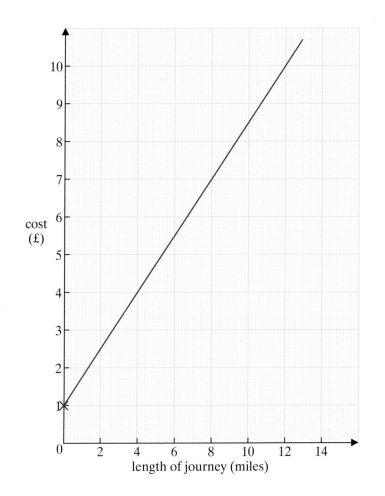

Use the graph to find the cost of a journey of length:

(a) 10 miles   **(b)** 4 miles

(c) 9 miles   **(d)** 1 mile

Hint: → 1 small sq. = 0.2 miles
      ↑ 1 small sq. = 10 p = £0.10

How far could you go for:

(e) £5   **(f)** £4

(g) £9   **(h)** £3.50

The cost is made up of a fixed charge plus an amount
for each mile.

(i) How much is the fixed charge?

3 A tap has been left running. This graph shows how much the water level rises.

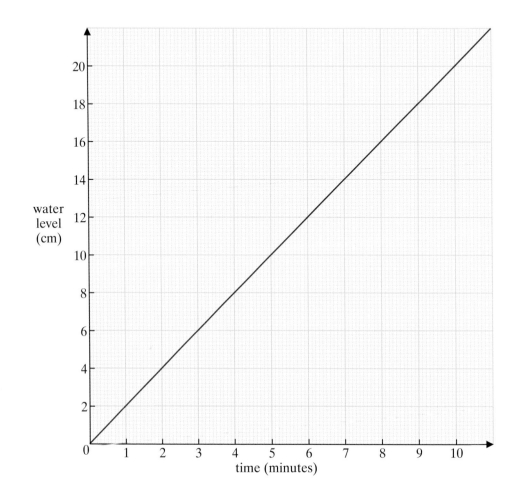

Use the graph to find how high the water is after:

(a) 2 minutes   **(b)** 4 minutes

(c) 6 minutes   **(d)** 7 minutes

After how long will the water be:

(e) 5 cm deep   **(f)** 10 cm deep

(g) 16 cm deep   **(h)** 19 cm deep.

4 A manufacturer makes metal pipes. This graph shows how to convert between the weight of metal and the length of pipe it produces.

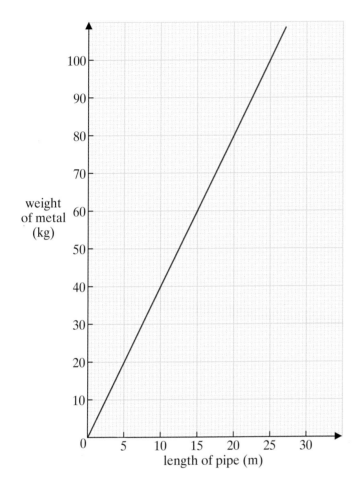

(a) Work out the scale on each axis.

Use the graph to find:

(b) the weight of a 12 metre pipe

(c) the weight of a 17 metre pipe

(d) the length of a pipe weighing 80 kg

(e) the length of a pipe weighing 25 kg.

5 This graph shows the relationship between the length of side of a square and its area.

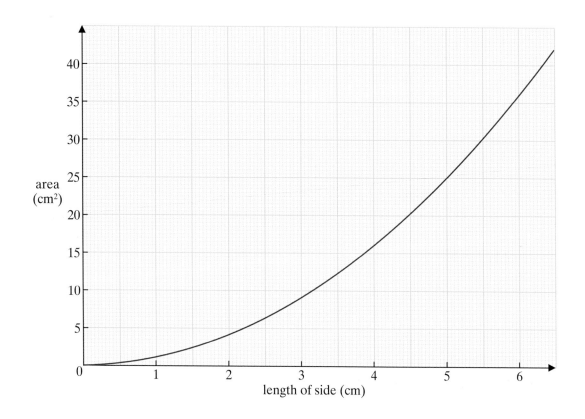

length of side (cm)

Use the graph to find:

(a) the area of a square with side 3 cm

(b) the area of a square with side 3.6 cm

(c) the area of a square with side 5.1 cm

(d) the length of one side of a square with area 25 cm^2

(e) the length of one side of a square with area 17 cm^2.

6 You will need graph paper.

Draw a horizontal axis 10 cm long. Label it 'length of side (cm)' and mark it from 0 to 50 cm in steps of 5 cm.

Draw a vertical axis 10 cm long. Label it 'perimeter of square (cm)' and mark it from 0 to 200 cm in steps of 20 cm.

Plot the points (0, 0) and (25, 100). Draw the straight line through these points.

Your graph shows the relationship between the length of one side of a square and its perimeter.

Using your graph, find:

(a) the perimeter of a square with side 35 cm
(b) the perimeter of a square with side 13 cm
(c) the length of one side of a square with perimeter 60 cm
(d) the length of one side of a square with perimeter 78 cm.

7 Use this information to draw a conversion graph between pounds (£) and francs (f):

Hint: Decide on your scale before you begin drawing.

$$£10 = 80\,f$$
$$£0 = 0\,f$$

Using your graph, find:

(a) how much 65 francs is in pounds
(b) how much 30 francs is in pounds
(c) how many francs are the same as £3
(d) how much £1 is in francs.

8 In a gardening shop 3 kg of fertiliser costs 75 p.
0 kg of fertiliser costs nothing!
Draw a straight line graph showing the relationship between weight of fertiliser and cost.

Hint: Look at the questions before deciding on your scale.

Using your graph, find:

(a) the cost of 7 kg of fertiliser
(b) the cost of 13 kg of fertiliser
(c) how much fertiliser you get for £3.50
(d) how much fertiliser you get for £1.

12.10 Graphs in all four quadrants

You need to be able to use graphs in all four quadrants.

Example 9

Ali uses this graph to convert temperatures between
degrees Fahrenheit (°F) and degrees Celsius (°C).

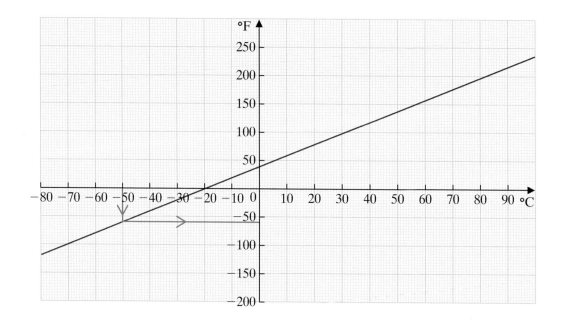

Use the graph to convert −50 °C into °F.

Read down from −50 °C and across to the vertical axis.

The answer is −60 °F.

Exercise 12J

Use the graph above to convert:

1 30 °C to °F

2 160 °F to °C

3 −10 °F to °C

4 −70 °C to °F

5 0 °C to °F.

Summary of key points

1 The horizontal coordinate is called the x-coordinate. The vertical coordinate is called the y-coordinate. You always write the x-coordinate first.

2 Each quarter of the coordinate grid is called a quadrant.

3 Vertical lines all have equation $x = \boxed{}$.

Horizontal lines all have equation $y = \boxed{}$.

4 To find the equation of a sloping line find a rule connecting the x-coordinate and the y-coordinate.

- If the line slopes diagonally upwards the equation will be $y = x + \boxed{}$ or $y = x - \boxed{}$.

- If the line slopes diagonally downwards the equation will be $x + y = \boxed{}$.

5 The intercept of a line is the point $(0, \boxed{})$ where the line crosses the y-axis. The number in the box is the value of y when $x = 0$.

6 Gradient is the mathematical word for steepness. The bigger the gradient, the steeper the slope.

- A line that slopes up has positive gradient.

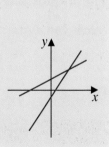

- A line that slopes down has negative gradient.

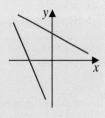

7 A graph shows a relationship on a coordinate grid.

13 Handling data

13.1 Questionnaires

One way of collecting data is to use a questionnaire.

The first step in designing a questionnaire is to decide exactly what you want to find out. Then think of appropriate questions to get this information.

It's better to keep the questions simple and give choices or tick boxes for the answers:

Can you swim?	
Yes	
No	

Which music do you like?	
Pop	
Soul	
Classical	
Other	

Time spent training on Monday	
None	
Less than 1 hour	
Between 1 and 2 hours	
Between 2 and 3 hours	
Over 3 hours	

Try to avoid personal or embarrassing questions.

These questions are unlikely to get a truthful answer:

Have you ever cheated in a test?

Yes ☐   No ☐

Do you wash every day?

Yes ☐   No ☐

Avoid questions that might influence the answer.

You agree milk is good for you?

Yes ☐   No ☐

Most people prefer salted peanuts, do you?

Yes ☐   No ☐

Bina and Tristan want to find out what year 8 pupils think of school dinners.

When they have decided on their questions, Bina and Tristan try them out on a few friends. This is called a **pilot survey**.

The pilot survey helps them check that the questions are simple, suitable and easy to answer.

SCHOOL DINNER SURVEY

Name . . . .

They decide *not* to ask for names. People may answer more honestly if they don't have to give their names.

How many times a week do you eat school dinners?

1 ☐   2 ☐   3 ☐   4 ☐   5 ☐

Roughly how much do you spend on each meal?

Under £1 ☐   £1–£2 ☐   £2–£3 ☐   over £3 ☐

How would you describe the choice of food available?

good ☐   OK ☐   poor ☐

Do you go to after-lunch clubs?

Yes ☐   No ☐

They remove this question because it isn't about school dinners.

How many times a week do you eat chips for lunch?

1 ☐   2 ☐   3 ☐   4 ☐   5 ☐

Once they are happy with their questionnaire Bina and Tristan need to decide how many people to ask.

There are around 200 pupils in year 8. It would take a long time to survey them all.

Bina and Tristan decide to give the questionnaire to a **sample** of 10% of year 8 pupils. They choose a sample of 20 pupils – 10 boys and 10 girls.

Exercise 13A

1 Decide whether each question is suitable for a questionnaire.

If not, give your reason and rewrite the question so it is suitable.

(a) You don't like cabbage, do you?

Yes ☐   No ☐

(b) What was the school match like?

Good ☐   Poor ☐   Lousy ☐

Fair ☐   OK ☐

(c) How many hours each week do you watch TV?

None ☐   1–5 ☐   6–10 ☐

11–15 ☐   > 15 ☐

(d) Have you ever stolen sweets from a shop?

Yes ☐   No ☐

(e) What is your favourite hobby? (Ring the answer)

Sport   Music   Reading   Art   None

(f) Do you drink coffee?

Often   Sometimes   Never

2 Design a questionnaire to find out about your classmates' holidays. You could ask about where they went, how they travelled, when they went, where they stayed or how much the holiday cost.

3 Design a questionnaire to find out about people's hobbies. You could ask how long they spend on their hobby, what skills they need or how long they have been doing it.

13.2 Charts and diagrams

You can show data in different types of charts.

■   **A pictogram uses symbols to show data.**

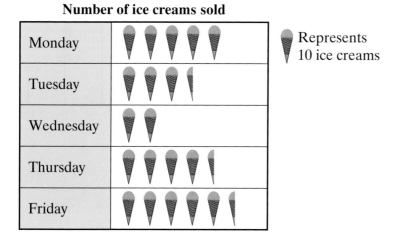

Number of ice creams sold

Represents 10 ice creams

■   **A bar chart uses bars or blocks to show discrete data.**

> Remember:
> **Discrete data** is data you count, for example number of people, cars or pens.

All the bars are the same width and there are gaps between them.

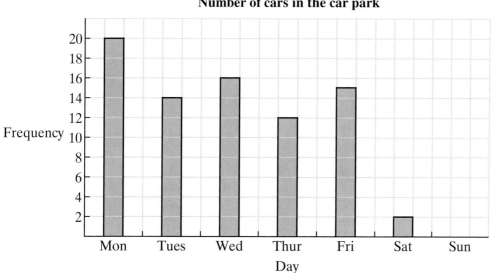

Number of cars in the car park

A bar-line graph uses lines instead of bars.

Number of pupils absent

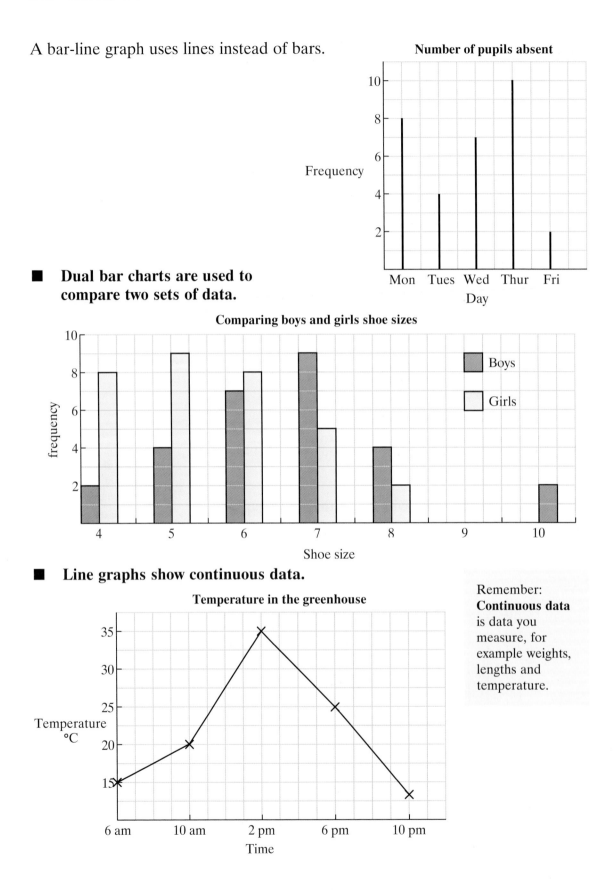

■ **Dual bar charts are used to compare two sets of data.**

Comparing boys and girls shoe sizes

■ **Line graphs show continuous data.**

Temperature in the greenhouse

Remember:
Continuous data is data you measure, for example weights, lengths and temperature.

Exercise 13B

1 Here are answers to the question 'On which day of the week were you born?'

Mon	Tues	Wed	Thur	Fri	Sat	Sun
12	10	18	14	16	20	14

(a) How many people's results are recorded?

(b) Draw a bar chart to represent this data.

(c) Draw a pictogram to illustrate this data.

Use 👤 to represent two people.

Remember:
In a bar chart use one axis for the item(s) and the other for the frequency. Label each axis clearly.

2 The table shows the number of letters received one week.

Mon	Tues	Wed	Thur	Fri	Sat
24	16	20	32	26	18

(a) Draw a bar-line graph to represent this data.

(b) Draw a pictogram to illustrate this data.
Use ⊞ to represent 4 letters.

3 The number of trains late each day in February were:

12	4	9	17	7	13	15
17	11	17	12	19	6	9
3	16	14	5	11	20	14
12	21	8	18	22	4	5

Using groups 0–4, 5–9, 10–14, etc. draw a bar graph.

Hint: You could draw a tally chart first.

4 The number of daily tuckshop sales in one half term were:

38	46	25	56	19	33	41	14	47
12	21	34	29	44	30	58	18	42
40	33	45	37	9	26	53	17	41
30	23	45	16	34	52	33	49	27

Choose appropriate groups and draw a bar graph.

5 The table shows the car sales figures for two garages:

	Jan	Feb	Mar	Apr	May	Jun
Carmart	14	12	22	16	20	18
Easybuy	12	16	20	22	14	16

(a) Draw a dual bar chart to represent this data.

(b) Comment on your result.

6 The table shows the average midday temperature, in °C, over a year. There is no data for June and October.

Month	Jan	Feb	Mar	Apr	May	July	Aug	Sept	Nov	Dec
Temperature	7	9	12	14	18	23	24	20	10	8

(a) Draw a line graph to illustrate this data.

(b) Estimate the temperature for June.
Explain how you arrived at your answer.

13.3 Stem and leaf diagrams

You have used tally charts to record data.
Stem and leaf diagrams are another way to do this.

Daniel collected data on the weekly wages in pounds of 20 people:

224, 258, 248, 247, 292, 265, 218, 210, 238, 262,

297, 286, 233, 258, 261, 286, 212, 226, 245, 281

First he recorded the data in a tally chart:

Wages	Tally	Frequency
210–219	|||	3
220–229	||	2
230–239	||	2
240–249	|||	3
250–259	||	2
260–269	|||	3
270–279		0
280–289	|||	3
290–299	||	2

Daniel realised that he could not read any individual values from this chart.

He made a new chart using groups as **stems**. The group 210–219 has the stem 21, since all the values in the group start with these two digits.

The stems for this data are:

21
22
23
24
25
26
27
28
29

Then Daniel added the **leaves**, the other part of the data.
He recorded 224 like this:

```
21 |
22 | 4
23 |
24 |
25 |
26 |
27 |
28 |
29 |
```

Here is Daniel's completed stem and leaf diagram:

```
21 | 8 0 2
22 | 4 6
23 | 8 3
24 | 7 5 8
25 | 8 8
26 | 5 2 1
27 |
28 | 6 6 1
29 | 2 7
```

Stem = £10

For the value 210 the stem is 21 and the leaf is 0.

There are no values in the range 270–279.

This shows that to read off the values you have to multiply the stem by 10 and add on the leaf.

■ **In a stem and leaf diagram all the individual values are recorded. You can read them off the diagram.**

To organize the data more, you can write the leaves in order:

```
21 | 0 2 8
22 | 4 6
23 | 3 8
24 | 5 7 8
25 | 8 8
26 | 1 2 5
27 |
28 | 1 6 6
29 | 2 7
```

Stem = £10

Exercise 13C

1 Draw a stem and leaf diagram for this data:

Heights in cm

154, 160, 171, 148, 139, 177, 162, 168, 155, 148

172, 156, 170, 149, 140, 181, 167, 158, 166, 149

Use these stems:

```
13 |
14 |
15 |
16 |
17 |
18 |
```

Stem = 10 cm

2 Draw a stem and leaf diagram for this data. Is this a good method of representing the data?

Lengths of insects in cm

1.2, 1.3, 1.4, 1.5, 1.1, 1.2, 1.4, 1.2,

1.6, 1.4, 1.7, 1.9, 1.5, 1.3, 1.5, 1.3

Use stem = 1.0 cm

3 Draw a stem and leaf diagram for this data:

Prices of motorbikes (£)

5995, 6925, 4835, 2660, 6450, 2775, 3950, 4995, 2950,

4500, 5325, 4650, 2995, 3150, 4000, 3500, 2875, 3425,

6250, 5600, 4895, 5325, 3995, 5250, 3850, 2995, 5500

4 Draw a stem and leaf diagram for this data:

Times to complete an obstacle course (seconds)

18.6, 17.3, 18.4, 19.3, 20.3, 22.5, 23.1, 23.0, 18.2

17.4, 19.5, 18.7, 20.4, 23.7, 22.5, 18.5, 24.3, 19.3

18.6, 17.2, 19.3, 22.6, 25.1, 17.9, 18.7, 16.9, 18.8

13.4 Histograms

■ **Histograms display grouped continuous data.**

Histograms look like bar charts but there are no gaps between the bars.

The bars must all be the same width for the height to show the data values.

The table shows the times children took to tie their shoelaces.

Time in seconds	Frequency
10 to less than 15 seconds	3
15 to less than 20 seconds	5
20 to less than 25 seconds	8
25 to less than 30 seconds	11
30 to less than 35 seconds	7

Here is the histogram for this data.

There is a bar for each group of data.

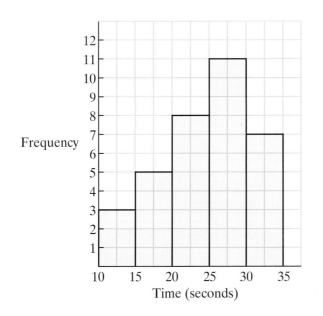

Exercise 13D

1 This histogram shows the times pupils took to do a tables test.

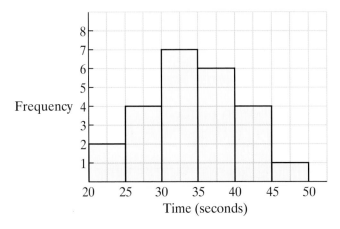

(a) How many pupils took less than 35 seconds?

(b) How many pupils took 40 seconds or over?

2 Draw a histogram for this data:

Distances travelled to school (km)

3.1, 0.5, 4.2, 2.5, 6.7, 4.6, 3.2, 4.5, 3.7, 2.6,
5.3, 7.3, 5.9, 2.5, 2.7, 5.4, 3.7, 8.5, 7.3, 3.5,
6.4, 8.2, 4.4, 7.5, 2.6, 5.3, 7.7, 4.1, 6.3, 1.5

Use groups '0 to less than 1', '1 to less than 2', etc.

3 The ages of workers in a factory are:

Age	18–23	24–29	30–35	36–41	42–47	48–53	54–59	60–65
Workers	12	18	22	20	26	30	28	24

(a) Draw a histogram to represent this data.

(b) Comment on your result.

Hint: Your first group will be '18 to less than 24'.

4 The table shows the amounts shoppers spent in a supermarket, rounded down to the nearest £.

Amount	20–29	30–39	40–49	50–59	60–69	70–79	80–89	90–99
Shoppers	4	6	3	8	10	12	7	4

Draw a histogram to represent this data.

5 The table gives the weights of tomatoes rounded down to the nearest gram.

Weight	10–19	20–29	30–39	40–49	50–59	60–69
Tomatoes	2	6	10	4	1	0

Draw a histogram for this data.

13.5 Frequency polygons

■ **You can use frequency polygons to compare two sets of data.**

You draw a frequency polygon by joining the mid-points of a histogram.

Example 1

These two histograms show the heights of year 8 pupils in different schools.

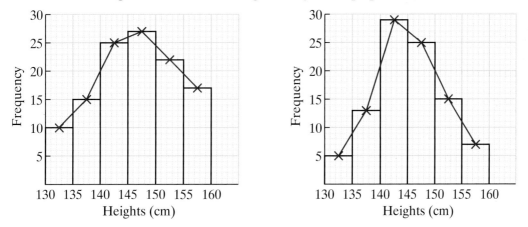

You can draw both frequency polygons on one graph to compare them.

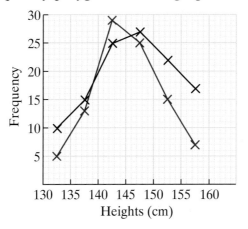

Exercise 13E

1 The table shows the frequency distribution of ages of members of a hockey club and a drama club.

Age	0–9	10–19	20–29	30–39	40–49	50–59	over 60
Hockey	8	22	30	34	25	18	10
Drama	2	10	18	28	32	27	20

(a) Draw a histogram for each.

(b) Draw a frequency polygon for each.

(c) Draw both polygons on the same graph.

(d) Comment on your result.

2 The table gives the frequency distribution of speeds of cars on a motorway and a trunk road.

Speed (mph)	30 to less than 40	40 to less than 50	50 to less than 60	60 to less than 70	70 to less than 80	80 to less than 90
Motorway	3	10	24	32	4	2
Trunk road	10	34	28	3	0	0

(a) Draw a histogram for each type of road.

(b) Draw a frequency polygon for each type of road.

(c) Draw both the frequency polygons on one graph.

(d) Comment on your result.

3 The table gives the heights in cm of shrubs grown in two different soils.

Height	25 to less than 30	30 to less than 35	35 to less than 40	40 to less than 45	45 to less than 50	55 to less than 60	60 to less than 65
Soil A	5	12	15	8	5	3	2
Soil B	6	9	10	18	4	2	1

(a) Draw a frequency polygon for each type of soil.

(b) Draw both the frequency polygons on one graph.

(c) Comment on your result.

4 The table gives the maths test results for two groups of pupils.

Mark	30–34	35–39	40–44	45–49	50–54	55–59	60–64	65–69	70–74
Group A	3	2	6	10	5	2	1	1	0
Group B	0	3	4	6	9	5	1	1	1

(a) Draw a frequency polygon for each group of pupils.

(b) Draw both the frequency polygons on one graph.

(c) Comment on your result.

13.6 Pie charts

■ **A pie chart shows how something is shared or divided up.**

Florence Nightingale cut a circular loaf of bread to show what proportion of the patients died in a hospital. She used it to illustrate the high death rate.

Example 2

Four students collect signatures for a petition to keep an animal rescue centre open.

Andrew gets 12 signatures, Brenda gets 24, Ceri gets 20 and Dipak gets 16.

Draw a pie chart to show this data.

Step 1: work out the total number of signatures.

$12 + 24 + 20 + 16 = 72$

Step 2: work out the angle for each signature.

The angle for one signature $= \dfrac{360°}{72} = 5°$

Remember: There are 360° in a circle.

Step 3: work out the angle for each student.
It is easiest to put the information in a table.

Name	Frequency	Angle
Andrew	12	$12 \times 5° = 60°$
Brenda	24	$24 \times 5° = 120°$
Ceri	20	$20 \times 5° = 100°$
Dipak	16	$16 \times 5° = 80°$

Step 4: draw a circle.
Draw segments with these angles to complete the pie chart.

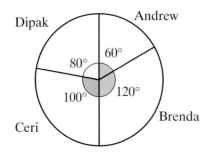

1 A rugby player has played for his country 60 times.
His team has won 35 games, drawn 6 games and lost
the rest.

(a) How many of the games were lost?

(b) Draw a pie chart to show the results of these 60
games.

2 The number of books lent out by a school library each
day is shown in the table.

Day	Mon	Tues	Wed	Thurs	Fri
Number of books lent	12	28	30	15	5

Draw a pie chart to show this information.

3 The table shows the average amount of money pupils
spent on different items during a day trip.

Item	Fairground rides	Sweets and snacks	Ice creams and drinks	Arcade games	Other
Amount	£3	£2	£1.50	£2.50	£1

Draw a pie chart to show this information.

4 The bar chart shows the number of pupils who were late during one week.

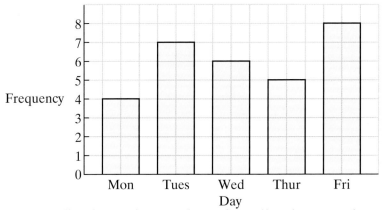

(a) Write down the number of pupils who were late for each day.

(b) Show this information on a pie chart.

5 This dual bar chart shows the number of boys and girls in years 9, 10 and 11 of a school.

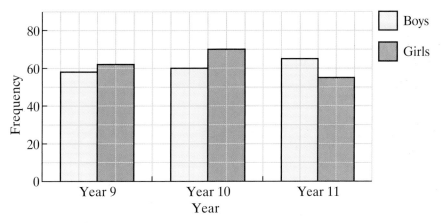

Draw a single pie chart with six sectors to represent this data.

6 In a survey 120 people were asked which food they preferred from

Indian, Chinese, Burger and fries, Fish and chips

The results are shown in the pie chart.

(a) The total frequency is 120. How many degrees represent each person?

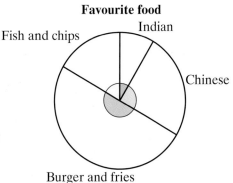

(b) Measure the angles of each sector and complete this table with numbers of people who chose each food.

You can use **Activity sheet 4** to help you measure the angles.

	Indian	Chinese	Burger and fries	Fish and chips
Angle				
Frequency				

13.7 Showing proportions and percentages on a pie chart

■ **You can draw a pie chart even if you do not know the total frequency or even the frequencies for each class.**

Example 3

A survey asked this question:

Do you think smoking is bad for you?

Yes ☐   No ☐   Don't know ☐

Of the people asked:

$\frac{1}{2}$ answered Yes

$\frac{1}{3}$ answered No

$\frac{1}{6}$ answered Don't Know

Show this information on a pie chart.

$\frac{1}{2}$ of the people said Yes.

So the angle for Yes is $\frac{1}{2} \times 360° = 180°$

$\frac{1}{3}$ of the people said No.

The angle for No is $\frac{1}{3} \times 360° = 120°$

The angle for Don't Know is $\frac{1}{6} \times 360° = 60°$

(Check: $180° + 120° + 60° = 360°$)

The pie chart is:

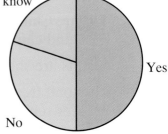

Example 4

In an election the Red party got 32% of the votes, the Blue party got 41% and the yellow party got 25% with 2% of papers spoilt.

Show this information on a pie chart.

Calculate the angle for the Red party.

Change 32% to a decimal.

$$32\% = \frac{32}{100} = 0.32$$

The angle for the Red party is $0.32 \times 360 = 115.2$ which is 115 to the nearest degree.

> You need to round some of the angles to the nearest degree.

Blue party	$0.41 \times 360 = 147.6$	$148°$
Yellow party	$0.25 \times 360 = 90$	$90°$
Spoilt papers	$0.02 \times 360 = 7.2$	$7°$

Check: $115 + 148 + 90 + 7 = 360$ ⟵ Make sure the total is 360°.

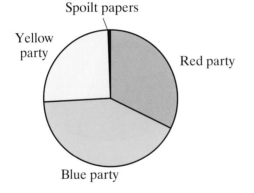

Exercise 13G

1   In a town the children have a choice of four schools.

$\frac{1}{4}$ of the children go to Holly Tree School,

$\frac{1}{5}$ of the children go to Shorelands School,

$\frac{1}{10}$ of the children go to Bristol Hall School

and the remainder go to Green Wood School.

(a) What fraction of the children go to Green Wood School?

(b) Draw a pie chart to show this information.

2 The table below shows the percentages of people choosing favourite colours.

Colour	Red	Blue	Yellow	Green	Black
Percentage	15	20	30	10	25

Draw a pie chart to show this information.

3 A group of teenagers were asked to choose their favourite football team.
They drew a pie chart to represent their results.

(a) Measure the angles and work out the percentage of the teenagers who chose each team.

(b) There were 40 teenagers in the sample.
Work out how many chose each team.

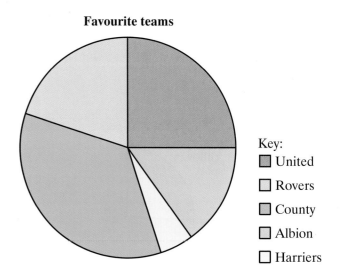

Favourite teams

Key:
■ United
□ Rovers
■ County
□ Albion
□ Harriers

4 A one-hour lesson consisted of:

an introduction for 12 minutes,
working in pairs for 15 minutes,
individual work for 20 minutes,
a final discussion for 10 minutes and
packing away books for 3 minutes.

(a) Draw a pie chart to show this information.
Mark the angles clearly.

(b) Represent this information on a different sort of graph or chart.

13.8 Scatter diagrams

To work out if two sets of data are related you can draw a
scatter diagram.

■   **A scatter diagram shows the relationship between two
sets of data.**

Neil measures the heights and weights of 9 of his friends.

These are his results:

Height (cm)	163	170	179	180	182	184	185	190	195
Weight (kg)	75	72	85	86	91	93	96	99	102

We can show this data on a scatter diagram by plotting the
height on the x-axis and the weight on the y-axis.

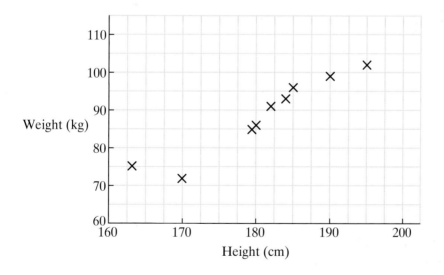

The graph shows an upward trend.

This means that the greater the height, the greater the
weight will be.

This type of trend is called **positive correlation**.

Correlation means
how two things
are related.

■   **There are three main kinds of correlation.**

You need to be able to recognise different kinds of correlation.

Positive correlation	Negative correlation	No correlation

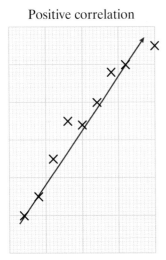

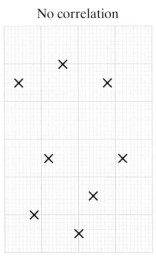

One quantity increases as the as the other increases.

One quantity increases as the as the other decreases.

There is no relationship between quantities.

Line of best fit

■ **The line of best fit on a scatter diagram shows the trend of the relationship between the two sets of data.**

The line of best fit is drawn as close as possible to the points on a scatter diagram, with roughly the same number of points above and below it.

This scatter diagram shows positive correlation. To draw the line of best fit put your ruler on the graph and move it until there are roughly the same number of points either side of it.

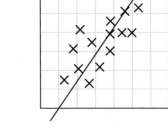

The line of best fit for a scatter diagram showing negative correlation is drawn in the same way.

To be more accurate, calculate the mean for each set of data. The line of best fit should pass through the point (Mean A, Mean B).

Example 6

The table gives the results of Alix's maths and science tests last year:

Test	1	2	3	4	5	6	7	8	9	10	11	12
Maths	38	54	45	53	70	64	42	66	78	72	78	70
Science	42	52	50	58	64	66	50	72	70	80	77	75

(a) Draw a scatter graph for this data and draw the line of best fit.

(b) Comment upon the correlation if any.

(c) If Alix scored 50 in a maths test what mark would you expect her to get in science?

(a)

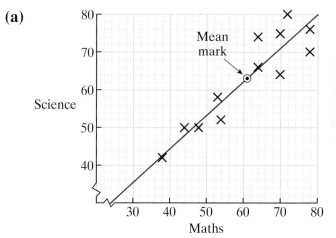

Mean maths mark $= 726 \div 12 = 60.5$

Mean science mark $= 756 \div 12 = 63$

The line of best fit passes through $(61, 63)$

(b) Positive correlation.

(c) Alix would get 53.

Exercise 13H

1 Results for mathematics and science tests are shown in the table.

Maths	28	35	42	56	61	73	78	82	85	91	93	98
Science	33	42	41	60	65	66	75	80	84	89	95	87

(a) Draw a scatter diagram to represent this data. (Both axes should go up to 100.)

(b) Draw the line of best fit.

(c) Comment upon the correlation.

2 The table shows the number of cups of soup sold per day and the average daily temperature in °C.

Temperature	0	23	11	32	15	4	16	20	1	30	18	12
Cups of soup	98	50	75	30	68	88	70	61	94	31	60	2

(a) Draw a scatter diagram to represent this data.

(b) Draw the line of best fit.

(c) Comment upon the correlation.

3 The table shows results of a group of fitness tests, marked out of 30.

Agility	14	21	26	9	16	22	11	24	10	28	6	19
Strength	12	20	25	7	12	18	10	22	9	25	6	17
Reaction	13	10	4	24	16	12	28	6	24	7	22	18

(a) Draw scatter diagrams for:
  - agility and strength
  - agility and reaction
  - strength and reaction

(b) Comment upon the correlation, if any.

4 The heights and weights of the Welsh rugby scrum are shown in the table:

Height (feet)	6.0	5.9	5.7	6.7	6.4	6.1	6.2	5.9
Weight (stones)	18.4	16.8	16.8	17.7	16.8	16.0	16.7	15.8

(a) Draw a scatter diagram to represent this data. (Your x-axis should go from 5.5 to 7.0 and your y-axis should go from 15 to 18.)

(b) Draw the line of best fit.

(c) Comment upon the correlation.

5 Every ten minutes Meryl noted down the number of birthday cakes left to be iced. The table shows her results:

Time (min)	10	20	30	40	50	60	70	80	90	100	110	120
Cakes left	80	75	69	61	53	46	39	31	24	17	8	0

(a) Draw a scatter diagram to represent this data.

(b) Draw the line of best fit.

(c) Comment upon the correlation.

6 For each of the following, sketch a possible scatter diagram you might get from a survey and state whether there would be a positive, negative or no correlation.

(a) Shoe size and height

(b) Engine size and fuel economy of a car

(c) Wages earned and time worked

(d) Age of person and time spent watching television

(e) Cost and distance travelled

(f) Distance travelled and fuel left.

Summary of key points

1 A pictogram uses symbols to show data.

2 A bar chart uses bars or blocks to show discrete data.

3 Dual bar charts are used to compare two sets of discrete data.

4 Line graphs show continuous data.

5 In a stem and leaf diagram all the individual values are recorded. You can read them off the diagram.

6 Histograms display grouped continuous data.

7 You can use frequency polygons to compare two sets of data.

8 A pie chart shows how something is shared or divided up.

9 You can draw a pie chart even if you do not know the frequencies for each class.

10 A scatter diagram shows the relationship between two sets of data.

11 There are three main kinds of correlation.

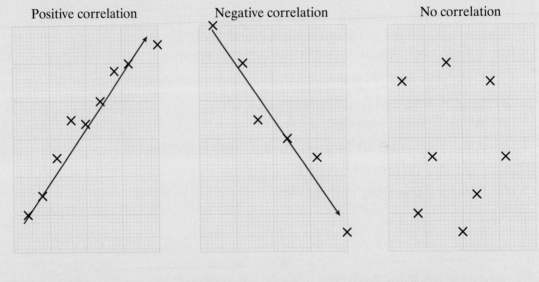

12 The line of best fit on a scatter diagram shows the trend of the relationship between the two sets of data.

14 Formulae and equations

The formula $F = G\,\dfrac{M_1 M_2}{d^2}$ is used to calculate the force of gravity.

It was discovered by Isaac Newton in the seventeenth century, and was used to land astronauts Neil Armstrong and Buzz Aldrin on the moon in 1969.

In this chapter you will practise solving equations and working out formulae.

Remember:
Formulae is the plural of formula.

14.1 Substituting into formulae

You need to be able to deal with situations where there are two operations in one formula.

Example 1

Lucy uses this word formula to work out her pay:

Pay = Hours worked × Rate of pay + Bonus

(a) Write this as a formula using letters.
(b) How much will Lucy earn for working 4 hours at a rate of pay of £7 an hour with a £5 bonus?

(a) The formula is

$P = HR + B$

Remember:
HR means $H \times R$

(b) Put the numbers into the formula:

$P = 4 \times 7 + 5$
$ = 28 + 5$
$ = 33$

Lucy earns £33.

Remember BIDMAS:
You always multiply before you add.

You can substitute into more difficult formulae.

Example 2

The perimeter of this rectangle is given
by the formula

$$P = 2(l + w)$$

Find the value of P if $l = 6\,cm$ and $w = 3\,cm$.

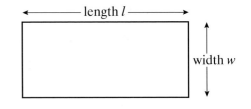

Put the numbers in the formula:

$$P = 2 \times (6 + 3)$$
$$= 2 \times 9$$
$$= 18$$

The value of P is 18 cm.

> **Remember BIDMAS:**
> Work out the
> brackets first.

Exercise 14A

Mr Greening uses this formula to work out how much to
pay his staff:

> *Pay = Hours worked × Rate of pay − Deductions*

> Deductions are
> taken away from
> people's pay for
> Income Tax and
> National
> Insurance.

1 Write this as a formula using letters.

2 Bimla works for 8 hours one day at a rate of pay of £5
an hour. She has deductions of £2. How much does she
earn that day?

3 Andrew works for 40 hours one week at a rate of pay
of £4 an hour. He has deductions of £25. How much
does he earn that week?

4 Abbas works for 12 hours one week at a rate of pay of
£4 an hour. He has deductions of £2.50. How much
does he earn for that week?

5 Naseema works for 12 hours one week at a rate of pay
of £2.50 an hour. She has deductions of £3.50. How
much does she earn that week?

6 Daphne uses the formula

Number of posts = length of fence in metres $\div\, 2 + 1$

to work out how many posts she needs to buy when she builds a fence.

(a) Write this as a formula using letters.

(b) Work out how many posts she needs to buy for a fence that is of length

    (i) 8 metres   **(ii)** 12 metres   **(iii)** 20 metres

7 Sam uses the formula

$$D = st$$

to work out how far he has travelled. D stands for the distance travelled in miles, s for the speed in miles per hour, and t for the time in hours. Use the formula to find D when

(a) $s = 30$ and $t = 3$

(b) $s = 50$ and $t = 4$

(c) $s = 70$ and $t = 3$

(d) $s = 23$ and $t = 2$

8 The formula $A = l^2$ is used to work out the area of a square. A stands for the area of the square and l for the length of one side. Use the formula to find A when

Remember:

l^2 means $l \times l$.

(a) $l = 6\,\text{cm}$

(b) $l = 8\,\text{cm}$

(c) $l = 12\,\text{m}$

(d) $l = 5\,\text{m}$

9 The area, A, of this shape is given by the formula

$$A = x^2 + \tfrac{1}{2}bx$$

Find the value of A when

(a) $x = 2$ and $b = 3$

(b) $x = 5$ and $b = 6$

(c) $x = 10$ and $b = 12$

(d) $x = 8$ and $b = 3$

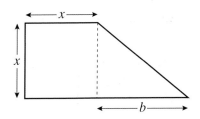

14.2 Writing your own formulae

Sometimes you will need to write your own formula.

Example 3

Write a formula for the perimeter, P, of this shape.

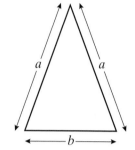

The perimeter is the distance around the shape. This will be

$$a + a + b \quad \text{or} \quad 2 \times a + b$$

The formula is $P = 2a + b$.

Example 4

Jade buys some bananas which cost 25p each. If b stands for the number of bananas she buys, write a formula for the total cost, C, in pence.

The total cost will be

$$25\text{p} \times \text{number of bananas bought}$$

The formula is $C = 25b$.

Exercise 14B

1 Write down a formula for the perimeter, P, of each of these shapes.

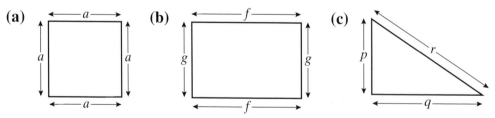

2 Write down a formula for the total cost in pence, C, of p pies at 40p each.

3 Write down a formula for the total cost in pence, C, of b bags of sweets at 20p each.

4 A rope on this boat is used to set the sails. It passes a distance d metres along the deck before going up one side of the mast and down the other.
The mast is h metres high. Write a formula for the total length of the rope in metres, L.

5 Ali has s sweets. He gives r of them to Ismat. Write down a formula for the number of sweets he has left, N.

6 John has w chocolate bars. He divides them equally between himself and his two sisters. He then gives one to his friend Keith.

(a) Write down a formula for the number of chocolate bars John has left, N.

Use your formula to find the value of N when

(b) $w = 6$ (c) $w = 15$

14.3 Solving equations

■ An *equation* is a mathematical sentence.
Every equation has a letter in it.
Finding a number value for that letter which makes the sentence true is called *solving the equation*.

The equation $x - 2 = 5$ is only true if $x = 7$. The **solution** to this equation is $x = 7$.

Sometimes you can solve an equation using number facts.

Example 5

Solve the equation $a + 4 = 7$.

You know that $3 + 4 = 7$.
The solution to this equation is $a = 3$.

You can solve equations in a more systematic way using algebra.

Example 6

Solve the equation $b + 7 = 9$.

Think of the equation as a pair of scales.

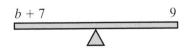

You must find a number value
for b which balances the scales.
You need b on its own on one side
of the scales.

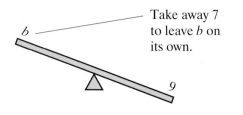

Take away 7
to leave b on
its own.

The other side of the scales is
too heavy.
What must you take away to
make them balance?

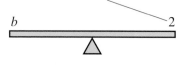

Take away 7 to
balance the scales.

The solution to this equation is $b = 2$.

You don't need to draw the scales every time.

Example 7

Solve the equation $x - 5 = 4$.

You need x on its own on one side of the equation.
Add 5 to both sides of the equation.

$$x - 5 + 5 = 4 + 5$$
$$x = 4 + 5$$
$$x = 9$$

Add 5 is the
inverse operation
of *subtract* 5, so
$$x - 5 + 5 = x$$

The solution to this equation is $x = 9$.

■ **You must always do the same thing to both sides of an equation.**

Exercise 14C

1 Solve these equations using number facts.

    (a) $p + 6 = 8$ **(b)** $q + 2 = 7$ **(c)** $r + 6 = 11$

    (d) $s - 3 = 3$ **(e)** $u - 1 = 8$ **(f)** $w - 7 = 2$

You should set
out your answers
in the same way
as **Example 7**.
Always write the
equals signs
underneath each
other.

2 Solve these equations using algebra.

    (a) $v - 4 = 5$ **(b)** $x + 3 = 5$ **(c)** $y + 6 = 13$

    (d) $z - 6 = 9$ **(e)** $a + 9 = 17$ **(f)** $b - 1 = 6$

    (g) $c - 3 = 1$ **(h)** $d + 8 = 11$

3 Solve these equations using algebra.

(a) $k + 26 = 41$ (b) $l - 19 = 12$

(c) $m + 8 = 103$ (d) $n + 14 = 21$

(e) $p - 17 = 81$ (f) $q + 106 = 193$

(g) $r - 11 = 92$ (h) $s - 72 = 9$

14.4 Equations with multiply and divide

You can solve more complicated equations in exactly the same way using algebra.

Example 8

Solve the equation $3c = 18$.

You need c on its own on one side of the equation.
Divide both sides of the equation by 3.

$$3 \times c = 18$$
$$3 \times c \div 3 = 18 \div 3$$
$$c = 18 \div 3$$
$$c = 6$$

The solution to this equation is $c = 6$.

Remember:
$6c$ means $6 \times c$.

Divide by 3 is the **inverse operation** of *multiply by 3*, so
$3 \times c \div 3 = c$

Exercise 14D

1 Solve these equations using algebra:

(a) $2p = 6$ (b) $2q = 8$ (c) $3r = 12$

(d) $5s = 5$ (e) $7u = 21$ (f) $3v = 36$

(g) $4w = 0$ (h) $2x = 3$

2 Solve the equation $d \div 5 = 4$.
Hint: *Multiply by 5* is the **inverse operation** of *divide by 5*,
so $d \div 5 \times 5 = d$

3 Solve these equations:

(a) $f \div 3 = 5$ (b) $g \div 2 = 3$ (c) $h \div 5 = 1$

(d) $j \div 3 = 8$ (e) $k \div 4 = 10$ (f) $l \div 5 = 6$

(g) $m \div 4 = 4$ (h) $n \div 7 = 0$

4   Solve these equations:

(a) $3m = 27$ (b) $2n = 36$ (c) $p \div 4 = 20$

(d) $q \div 3 = 3$ (e) $\dfrac{n}{6} = 2$ (f) $\dfrac{q}{5} = 3$

(g) $\dfrac{t}{6} = 12$ (h) $\dfrac{u}{11} = 4$

Remember:

$\dfrac{n}{6}$ means $n \div 6$

14.5 Equations with two operations

You will need to be able to solve equations with two operations.

Example 9

Solve the equation $3p + 2 = 20$.

You need p on its own on one side of the equation. Subtract 2 from both sides of the equation.

$$3p + 2 - 2 = 20 - 2$$
$$3p = 18$$

Divide both sides of the equation by 3.

$$3p \div 3 = 18 \div 3$$
$$p = 6$$

The solution to this equation is $p = 6$.

Remember:
You must always do the same thing to both sides of the equation.

Example 10

Solve the equation $\dfrac{q}{4} - 2 = 6$.

Add 2 to both sides of the equation.

$$\frac{q}{4} - 2 + 2 = 6 + 2$$

$$\frac{q}{4} = 8$$

Multiply both sides of the equation by 4.

$$\frac{q}{4} \times 4 = 8 \times 4$$

$$q = 32$$

The solution to this equation is $q = 32$.

Exercise 14E

1 Solve these equations:

(a) $3e + 4 = 13$ (b) $2f + 7 = 9$

(c) $4g + 4 = 12$ (d) $5h + 8 = 18$

(e) $5i + 1 = 16$ (f) $6j + 2 = 26$

(g) $7k + 12 = 26$ (h) $2l + 5 = 23$

2 Solve these equations:

(a) $3m - 3 = 12$ (b) $2n - 2 = 12$

(c) $5p - 12 = 8$ (d) $2q - 5 = 9$

(e) $4r - 8 = 16$ (f) $3s - 7 = 20$

(g) $10t - 20 = 80$ (h) $11u - 6 = 38$

3 Solve these equations:

(a) $\dfrac{v}{6} - 1 = 3$ (b) $\dfrac{w}{2} - 2 = 6$

(c) $\dfrac{x}{3} - 3 = 8$ (d) $\dfrac{y}{7} - 4 = 16$

4 Solve these equations:

(a) $\dfrac{p}{5} + 9 = 14$ (b) $\dfrac{q}{3} + 2 = 5$

(c) $\dfrac{r}{8} + 7 = 17$ (d) $\dfrac{t}{2} + 15 = 32$

14.6 Equations with a letter on both sides

Sometimes the letter will appear on both sides of the equation.

■ **When solving equations with the letter on both sides, always keep the letter on the side of the equation with the biggest number of letters.**

Example 11

Solve the equation

$$5a + 4 = 2a + 16$$

You need the letter on one side of the equation.
Subtract $2a$ from both sides of the equation.

$$5a + 4 - 2a = 2a + 16 - 2a$$
$$3a + 4 = 16$$

2a is smaller than 5a so you keep the letter on the left hand side of the equation.

Now solve the equation in the normal way.

$$3a + 4 - 4 = 16 - 4$$
$$3a = 12$$
$$3a \div 3 = 12 \div 3$$
$$a = 4$$

The solution to this equation is $a = 4$.

Example 12

Solve the equation

$$16 - 4p = 3p - 5.$$

Add $4p$ to both sides of the equation.

$$16 - 4p + 4p = 3p - 5 + 4p$$
$$16 = 7p - 5$$

−4p is smaller than 3p so you keep the letter on the right hand side of the equation.

You can write this as

$$7p - 5 = 16$$

Now solve the equation in the normal way.

$$7p - 5 + 5 = 16 + 5$$
$$7p = 21$$
$$7p \div 7 = 21 \div 7$$
$$p = 3$$

The solution to this equation is $p = 3$.

Exercise 14F

1 Solve these equations by keeping the letter on the left hand side of the equation:

(a) $3x + 2 = 2x + 5$ (b) $5p + 4 = 3p + 10$

(c) $6q - 3 = 2q + 9$ (d) $3t - 4 = 6 - 2t$

2 Solve these equations by keeping the letter on the right hand side of the equation:

(a) $2d + 6 = 5d - 12$ (b) $3f + 4 = 5f - 6$

(c) $4g + 1 = 6g - 3$ (d) $5 - 2h = 7h - 13$

3 Solve these equations:

(a) $5p + 3 = 4p + 5$ (b) $2q + 12 = 5q + 3$

(c) $3r + 10 = 5r + 2$ (d) $6s - 2 = 4s + 6$

(e) $6m - 5 = 19 - 2m$ (f) $29 - 9n = 4n + 3$

(g) $12 - j = 6 + j$ (h) $18 + 2k = 33 - k$

Remember: Keep the letter on the side of the equation with the biggest number of letters.

14.7 Equations with brackets

You can solve equations with brackets in them by multiplying out the brackets.

For a reminder on multiplying out brackets see chapter 10.

■ **When solving equations with brackets, always multiply out the brackets first.**

Example 13

Solve the equation

$$2(3a + 5) = 34.$$

Multiply out the brackets.

$$6a + 10 = 34$$

Now solve the equation in the normal way.

$$6a + 10 - \mathbf{10} = 34 - \mathbf{10}$$
$$6a = 24$$
$$6a \div \mathbf{6} = 24 \div \mathbf{6}$$
$$a = 4$$

The solution to this equation is $a = 4$.

Example 14

Solve the equation

$$4(3x + 2) + 5 = 31 - 2(x - 5)$$

Multiply out the brackets.

$$12x + 8 + 5 = 31 - 2x + 10$$
$$12x + 13 = 41 - 2x$$

Now solve the equation in the normal way.

$$12x + 13 + 2x = 41 - 2x + 2x$$
$$14x + 13 = 41$$
$$14x + 13 - 13 = 41 - 13$$
$$14x = 28$$
$$14x \div 14 = 28 \div 14$$
$$x = 2$$

The solution to this equation is $x = 2$.

Exercise 14G

1 Solve these equations:
   (a) $2(p + 1) = 6$ (b) $3(q - 6) + 4 = 10$
   (c) $3(2r + 1) - 11 = 7$ (d) $5(3s - 1) - 7 = 18$

2 Solve these equations:
   (a) $5(e + 12) = 4e + 72$ (b) $2(f + 3) = 3(f - 6)$
   (c) $5(2b - 2) = 2(3b + 15)$ (d) $3(2a - 4) = 2(2a + 6)$
   (e) $4(3x + 1) = 2x + 9$ (f) $5y + 20 = 4(y - 5)$
   (g) $3(4c - 6) = 5(2c + 5)$ (h) $5(x + 7) = 2 - 2(2x - 4)$

3 Solve these equations:
   (a) $4(p + 2) + 5 = 2(3p + 1) - 3$
   (b) $8(q + 2) - 1 = 3(3q - 1)$
   (c) $6(4 - 2n) = 2(n - 1) - n$
   (d) $-2(3 - 3n) - 1 = 2 - 3n$
   (e) $6(8v + 3) = 4(2v - 3) + 10$
   (f) $7 - 2(m + 1) = 4(2m - 1) - 1$
   (g) $6(t + 3) - 2t = 3(4t - 1) + 5$
   (h) $2(r + 9) = 3(4r + 6) - 5$

14.8 Inequalities

There are lots of apples, but there are
only a few bananas. If *a* is the number
of apples and *b* is the number of
bananas, then ***a* is greater than *b*.**
You can write this as ***a* > *b*.**

■   **> means *greater than*,
   < means *less than*.**

The thinner end points
towards the smaller number.
The thicker end points
towards the larger number.

Example 15

Put the correct sign between these pairs of numbers to
make a true statement:

(a) 6, 7

(b) 8, 5

(a) 6 is less than 7

$$6 < 7$$

(b) 8 is greater than 5

$$8 > 5$$

Example 16

Write down the values of *x* that are whole numbers and
satisfy these inequalities:

$$x > 2 \quad \text{and} \quad x < 7$$

$x > 2$ so the numbers must be bigger than 2:

   3, 4, 5, 6, 7, 8 . . .

$x < 7$ so the numbers must stop before 7.

The answer is 3, 4, 5, 6.

A number **satisfies**
an inequality if it
makes that
inequality true.

$x = 3$ **satisfies** the
inequality $x < 7$
because $3 < 7$.

Exercise 14H

1 Put the correct sign between these pairs of numbers to
make a true statement:

    (a) 4, 7   **(b)** 5, 2   **(c)** 12, 8   **(d)** 6, 6

    (e) 15, 8   **(f)** 3, 24   **(g)** 10, 3   **(h)** 0, 0.1

    (i) 6, 0.7   **(j)** 4.5, 4.5   **(k)** 0.2, 0.5   **(l)** 4.8, 4.79

2 Write down whether these statements are true or false.
If they are false write down the correct sign between
the numbers:

(a) $6 > 4$ (b) $2 > 6$ (c) $6 > 6$ (d) $6 > 8$

(e) $6 < 4$ (f) $8 = 14$ (g) $7 < 6.99$ (h) $6 > 6.01$

(i) $7 < 0$ (j) $4 < 4$ (k) $6 = 4$ (l) $6 > 0.84$

3 Write down the values of x that are whole numbers and
satisfy these inequalities:

(a) $x > 4$ and $x < 6$ (b) $x > 3$ and $x < 8$

(c) $x > 0$ and $x < 4$ (d) $x > 3$ and $x < 6$

(e) $x > 1$ and $x < 4$ (f) $x > 2$ and $x < 6$

(g) $x < 4$ and $x > 1$ (h) $x < 7$ and $x > 3$

(i) $x < 5$ and $x > 0$ (j) $x < 8$ and $x > 2$

(k) $x < 10$ and $x > 5$ (l) $x < 8$ and $x > 6$

14.9 Inequalities on a number line

You can show inequalities by shading a number line.

Example 17

Draw a number line from 0 to 10. Shade in the inequality

$x > 4$

x is greater than 4. You shade all the numbers to the right
of 4:

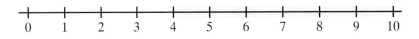

Example 18

Draw a number line from 0 to 10. Shade in the inequalities

$x > 3$ and $x < 8$

x is greater than 3 and less than 8. You shade in the
numbers between 3 and 8.

You can write
these inequalities

as $3 < x < 8$

This means x lies
between 3 and 8.

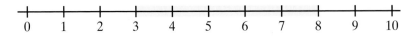

Exercise 14I

1 Draw 6 number lines from 0 to 10. Shade in these inequalities:

   (a) $x > 6$ (b) $x > 5$

   (c) $x < 4$ (d) $x > 8$

   (e) $x < 6$ (f) $x > 9$

2 Draw 6 number lines from 0 to 10. Shade in these inequalities:

   (a) $x > 3$ and $x < 7$ (b) $x > 5$ and $x < 8$

   (c) $x > 4$ and $x < 6$ (d) $x > 5$ and $x < 9$

   (e) $x > 3$ and $x < 5$ (f) $x > 2$ and $x < 8$

3 Draw 6 number lines from 0 to 10. Shade in these inequalities:

   (a) $4 < x < 7$ (b) $2 < x < 5$

   (c) $5 < x < 6$ (d) $7 < x < 9$

   (e) $1 < x < 6$ (f) $5 < x < 7$

4 Write down the inequalities represented by the shading on these number lines:

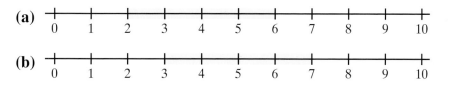

(a)

(b)

14.10 Solving equations by trial and improvement

For some equations it is very difficult, or even impossible, to find an exact solution.

You can get very close to the solution by guessing an answer and then improving your guess. This is called **solving the equation by trial and improvement**.

Example 19

Solve $x^2 - x = 9$ by trial and improvement.
Give your answer correct to one decimal places.

Try $x = 1$:

> $1^2 - 1 = 0$ Too small.

Try $x = 10$:

> $10^2 - 10 = 90$ Too big.

> Try simple values of x first.
> $x = 1, x = 5$ and $x = 10$ are easy to work out.

Too small | The answer must lie between 1 and 10. | Too big

$$0 \quad 1 \quad 2 \quad 3 \quad 4 \quad 5 \quad 6 \quad 7 \quad 8 \quad 9 \quad 10$$

Try $x = 5$:

> $5^2 - 5 = 20$ Too big.

Try $x = 3$:

> $3^2 - 3 = 6$ Too small.

Try $x = 4$:

> $4^2 - 4 = 12$ Too big.

Too small | The answer must lie between 3 and 4. | Too big | Too big

$$3 \quad 3.1 \ 3.2 \ 3.3 \ 3.4 \ 3.5 \ 3.6 \ 3.7 \ 3.8 \ 3.9 \quad 4 \quad 4.1 \ 4.2 \ 4.3 \ 4.4 \ 4.5 \ 4.6 \ 4.7 \ 4.8 \ 4.9 \quad 5$$

Try $x = 3.5$:

> $3.5^2 - 3.5 = 8.75$ Too small.

Try $x = 3.7$:

> $3.7^2 - 3.7 = 9.99$ Too big.

Try $x = 3.6$:

> $3.6^2 - 3.6 = 9.36$ Too big.

> Use a calculator for more complicated values of x.

Too small | Too big | Too big

$$3.4 \quad 3.45 \quad 3.5 \quad 3.55 \quad 3.6 \quad 3.65 \quad 3.7$$

The solution correct to one decimal place is either $x = 3.5$ or $x = 3.6$.

To find out which is the closest you must check half way between them.

> $3.55^2 - 3.55 = 9.0525$ Too big.

So the answer must lie between 3.5 and 3.55.

The solution correct to one decimal place is $x = 3.5$.

> You should always work with one more decimal place than is needed in the answer.

You should set out your answers in the form of a table.

Example 20

Solve $2x^2 + x = 18$ by trial and improvement. Give your answer correct to two decimal places.

Value of x	Value of $2x^2 + x$	Results compared to 18
1	3	Too small
10	210	Too big
5	55	Too big
3	21	Too big
2	10	Too small
2.5	15	Too small
2.8	18.48	Too big
2.7	17.28	Too small
2.75	17.875	Too small
2.77	18.1158	Too big
2.76	17.9952	Too small
2.765	18.05545	Too big

Solving equations by trial and improvement is an example of **numerical method**.

When you solve an equation with algebra you are using an **analytical method**.

This value of x lets you check whether 2.77 or 2.76 is the closest answer.

The solution correct to two decimal places is $x = 2.76$.

Exercise 14J

1 Solve these equations by trial and improvement. Give your answers correct to one decimal place.

Remember:
$x^3 = x \times x \times x.$

   (a) $x^2 = 10$ (b) $x^2 = 15$ (c) $x^3 = 30$
   (d) $x^2 + x = 20$ (e) $x^2 + x = 11$ (f) $x^2 - x = 21$

2 Solve these equations by trial and improvement. Give your answers correct to two decimal places.

   (a) $x^3 = 25$ (b) $x^2 = 8$ (c) $x^3 = 20$
   (d) $x^2 - x = 15$ (e) $x^3 + x = 4$ (f) $x^2 + x = 35$
   (g) $x^2 + 2x = 20$ (h) $x^2 - 3x = 32$ (i) $x^2 + 5x = 100$

3 A square has an area of $40\,\text{cm}^2$. What is the length of each side? Give your answer correct to two decimal places.

4 The area of this rectangle, A, is given by the formula

$$A = x^2 + 3x + 2$$

Find the value of x if $A = 50\,\text{cm}^2$.
Give your answer correct to two decimal places.

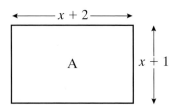

Summary of key points

1 An equation is a mathematical sentence.
Every equation has a letter in it.
Finding a number value for that letter which makes the sentence true is called solving the equation.

2 You must always do the same thing to both sides of an equation.

3 When solving equations with the letter on both sides, always keep the letter on the side of the equation with the biggest number of letters.

4 When solving equations with brackets, always multiply out the brackets first.

5 > means greater than.
< means less than.

15 Perimeter, area and volume

15.1 Perimeter and area

Yvonne is buying new carpets for her house.
For her bathroom she needs:

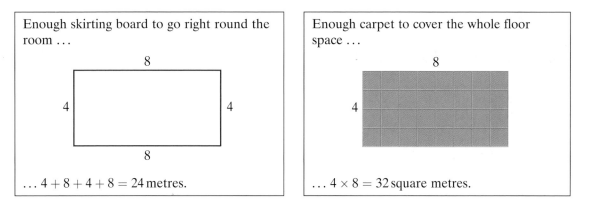

Enough skirting board to go right round the room …

... $4 + 8 + 4 + 8 = 24$ metres.

Enough carpet to cover the whole floor space …

... $4 \times 8 = 32$ square metres.

- ■ **The distance around a flat shape is its perimeter.**
- ■ **The space covered by a flat shape is its area.**

You can use these formulae for finding the perimeter or area of a rectangle:

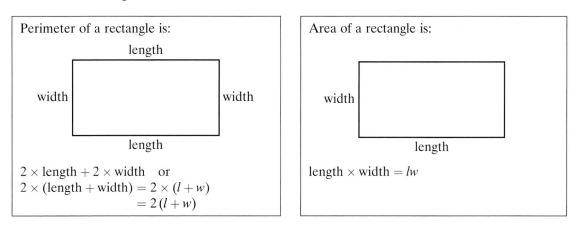

Perimeter of a rectangle is:

$2 \times \text{length} + 2 \times \text{width}$ or
$2 \times (\text{length} + \text{width}) = 2 \times (l + w)$
$= 2(l + w)$

Area of a rectangle is:

$\text{length} \times \text{width} = lw$

For any rectangle:

- ■ **Perimeter is 2 × (length + width) or $2(l + w)$**
- ■ **Area is length × width or lw**

Example 1

This is the plan of Yvonne's lounge:

Work out the total cost to replace
the carpet and skirting board if:

(a) the skirting board costs 40p per metre
(b) the carpet costs £12.00 per square metre.

The perimeter of the room is:

$$5 + 2 + 2 + 2 + 3 + 4 = 18 \text{ metres}$$

Yvonne needs 18 metres of skirting board.
The cost will be $18 \times 40p = 720p$ or £7.20

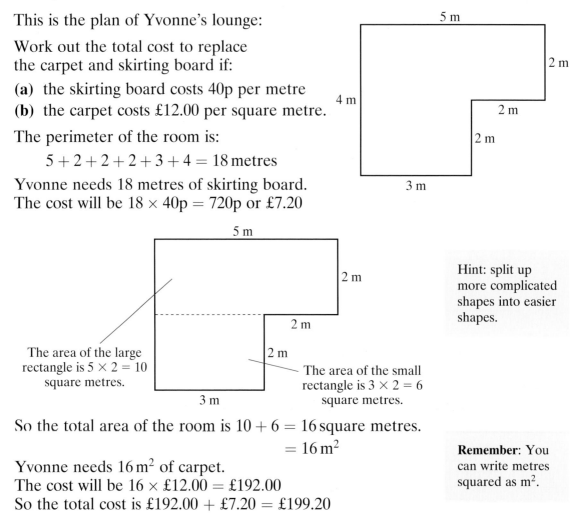

Hint: split up
more complicated
shapes into easier
shapes.

The area of the large
rectangle is $5 \times 2 = 10$
square metres.

The area of the small
rectangle is $3 \times 2 = 6$
square metres.

So the total area of the room is $10 + 6 = 16$ square metres.
$$= 16 \text{ m}^2$$

Yvonne needs 16 m^2 of carpet.
The cost will be $16 \times £12.00 = £192.00$
So the total cost is $£192.00 + £7.20 = £199.20$

Remember: You
can write metres
squared as m^2.

Exercise 15A

1 Work out the perimeter and area of these shapes all
   lengths are in centimetres:

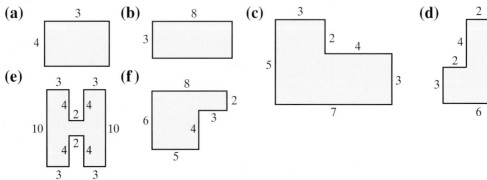

2 Mrs Healy is decorating her lounge.
The carpet costs £15 per square metre.
The skirting board costs 60 pence per metre.
Work out:

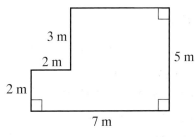

(a) the total length of skirting board needed

(b) the total area of carpet required

(c) the total cost of the carpet and the skirting board.

3 The perimeter of this rectangle is 26 cm.

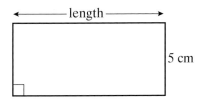

Work out:

(a) the length of the rectangle

(b) the area of the rectangle.

4 **Investigation**: Work out the largest possible area for a rectangle with a perimeter of 100 cm. Show all your working.

15.2 Triangles, trapeziums and parallelograms

You can use what you know about rectangles to find the areas of these shapes.

Triangles

The area of a triangle is half the area of the surrounding rectangle.

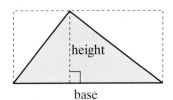

$$\text{Area of a triangle} = \tfrac{1}{2} \times \text{area of rectangle}$$

$$= \tfrac{1}{2} \times \text{base} \times \text{height}$$

For any triangle:

You should always use the perpendicular height in the equation for the area of a triangle.

■ **Area of a triangle** $= \tfrac{1}{2} \times$ **base** $\times$ **height**

Trapeziums

A trapezium is a shape with two parallel sides.
You can find the area by making it into a rectangle:

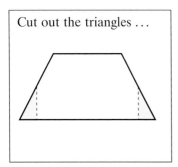

Cut out the triangles ...

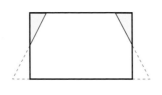

move them up here to make a rectangle with the same area as the trapezium ...

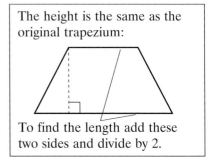

The height is the same as the original trapezium:

To find the length add these two sides and divide by 2.

For any trapezium:

■ **Area of a trapezium** $= \dfrac{(\textbf{base} + \textbf{top side})}{2} \times \textbf{height}$

Parallelograms

A parallelogram is a shape with both pairs of opposite sides parallel.

You can think of a parallelogram as being made up of two equal triangles.

So the area of a parallelogram is 2 lots of $\frac{1}{2}$ base × height.

■ **Area of a parallelogram** $=$ **base** × **height**

Area of a kite

This kite has length 20 cm, width 8 cm.

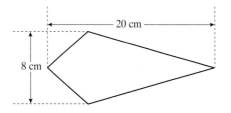

20 cm

8 cm

Draw the kite in a rectangle with the same dimensions:

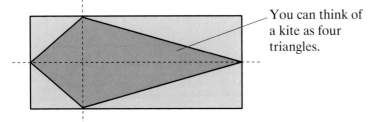

You can think of a kite as four triangles.

Each triangle's area is $\frac{1}{2} \times$ length $\times$ width so the area of the kite is also $\frac{1}{2} \times$ length $\times$ width.

$$\text{Area} = \frac{1}{2} \times 20 \times 8$$
$$= \quad 10 \quad \times 8 = 80\,\text{cm}^2$$

For any kite:

■ **Area of a kite $= \frac{1}{2} \times$ length $\times$ width**

Example 2

Work out these areas:

(a)

(b)

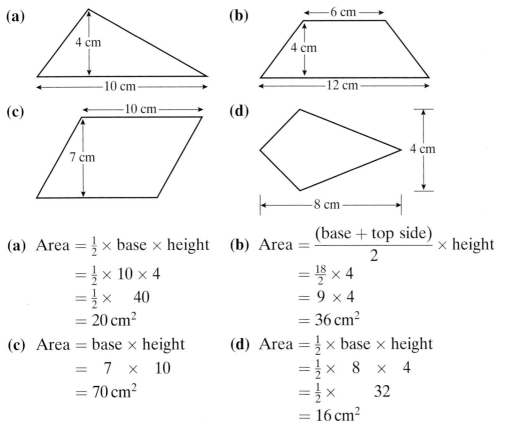

(c)

(d)

(a) Area $= \frac{1}{2} \times$ base $\times$ height

$\qquad = \frac{1}{2} \times 10 \times 4$

$\qquad = \frac{1}{2} \times \quad 40$

$\qquad = 20\,\text{cm}^2$

(b) Area $= \dfrac{(\text{base} + \text{top side})}{2} \times \text{height}$

$\qquad = \frac{18}{2} \times 4$

$\qquad = 9 \times 4$

$\qquad = 36\,\text{cm}^2$

(c) Area $=$ base $\times$ height

$\qquad = \quad 7 \quad \times \quad 10$

$\qquad = 70\,\text{cm}^2$

(d) Area $= \frac{1}{2} \times$ base $\times$ height

$\qquad = \frac{1}{2} \times \quad 8 \quad \times \quad 4$

$\qquad = \frac{1}{2} \times \qquad 32$

$\qquad = 16\,\text{cm}^2$

Example 3

Work out the area of the shaded region:

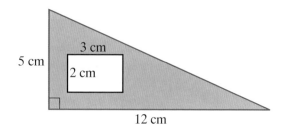

The area of the triangle is:

$$\tfrac{1}{2} \times 5 \times 12 = \tfrac{1}{2} \times 60$$
$$= 30 \, \text{cm}^2$$

The area of the rectangle is:

$$3 \times 2 = 6 \, \text{cm}^2$$

So the shaded area is:

$$30 - 6 = 24 \, \text{cm}^2$$

Exercise 15B

1 Work out the area of these shapes:

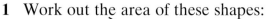

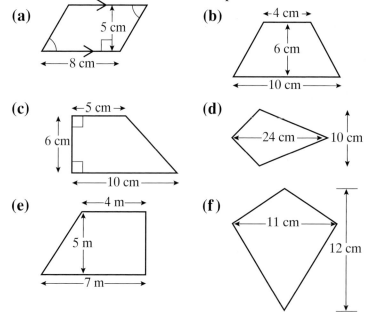

2 The parallelogram and the square have equal areas.

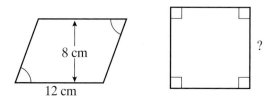

How long must the sides of the square be?

3 Work out the area of the shaded region.

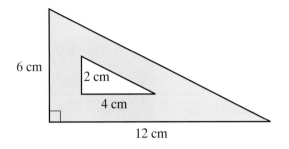

4 Work out the area of this floor space:

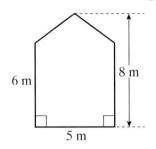

5 The coordinates of triangle ABC are: (1, 1), (7, 1) and (3, 5).
Draw the triangle and find its area.

6 Work out the area of this shape:

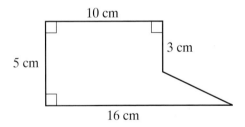

A rectangle of equal area is 7 cm wide.
Work out the length of this rectangle.

7 This flag is blue with a white kite.

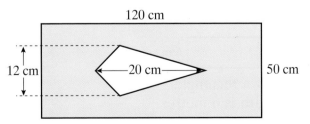

Work out the area of the blue region.

15.3 Mixing units

You need to be able to work out areas where the measurements use different units.

The Bayeaux Tapestry is 70 m long and 51 cm wide

Example 4

Work out the area of this triangle in:

(a) cm^2 **(b)** m^2

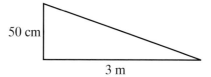

(a) Convert the metres to centimetres:

$$3\,\text{m} = 300\,\text{cm}$$

Now work out the area.

$$\begin{aligned}
\text{Area} &= \tfrac{1}{2} \times \text{length} \times \text{width} \\
&= \tfrac{1}{2} \times \quad 300 \quad \times \quad 50 \\
&= \tfrac{1}{2} \times \qquad\quad 15\,000 \\
&= 7500\,\text{cm}^2
\end{aligned}$$

(b) Convert the centimetres to metres:

$$50\,\text{cm} = 0.5\,\text{m}$$

Now work out the area.

$$\begin{aligned}
\text{Area} &= \tfrac{1}{2} \times \text{length} \times \text{width} \\
&= \tfrac{1}{2} \times \quad 3 \quad \times \quad 0.5 \\
&= \tfrac{1}{2} \times \qquad\quad 1.5 \\
&= 0.75\,\text{m}^2
\end{aligned}$$

Exercise 15C

1

2.3 km

6 m

This pathway is in the shape of a rectangle.
Its length is 2.3 kilometres, width is 6 metres.
Work out the area of the pathway in:

(a) m^2 **(b)** km^2

Remember to convert all the units before you start.

2 Work out the area of each rectangle. Give the units of your answer.

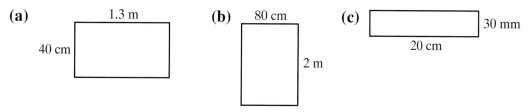

(a) 1.3 m, 40 cm

(b) 80 cm, 2 m

(c) 30 mm, 20 cm

3 When it is completely unwrapped a tape measure is rectangular:

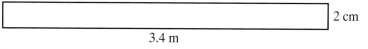

2 cm

3.4 m

The tape is 3.4 metres long and 2 cm wide.
Work out the area of the tape giving your answer in:

(a) cm^2 **(b)** m^2

4 Work out the area of each of these triangles.
Give the units of each answer.

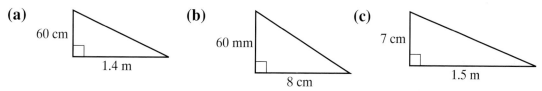

(a) 60 cm, 1.4 m

(b) 60 mm, 8 cm

(c) 7 cm, 1.5 m

5 Work out the area of each parallelogram.
Give each answer in at least two sets of units.

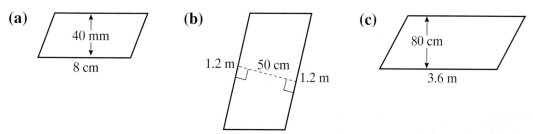

(a) 40 mm, 8 cm

(b) 1.2 m, 50 cm, 1.2 m

(c) 80 cm, 3.6 m

6 This flag is rectangular with a white parallelogram.
Work out:

(a) the area of the whole flag

(b) the area of the white parallelogram

(c) the area of the red region.

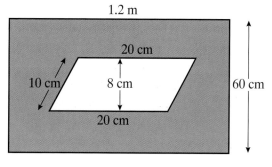

1.2 m

20 cm

10 cm

8 cm

60 cm

20 cm

7 ABCD is a parallelogram

AB = DC = 15 cm

AD = CB = 12 cm

The perpendicular distance between
AB and CD = 8 cm

Work out:

(a) the area of the parallelogram

(b) the perpendicular distance between AD and BC

15.4 Introducing pi

Thousands of years ago mathematicians
found a very important property of circles:

$$\frac{\text{circumference of a circle}}{\text{diameter}} = \text{a constant number}$$

This number is the same for any circle.

The constant number is the Greek letter pi: π.
Its value is 3.14 to 2 decimal places.

π is pronounced
'pie'.

You can use π to find the circumference and
area of a circle:

■ **circumference of a circle = $\pi \times$ diameter**

$$= 2 \times \pi \times \text{radius} \quad \text{or} \quad 2\,\pi r$$

■ **area of a circle = $\pi \times$ radius^2**

$$= \pi r^2$$

It is not possible to write π accurately in numbers,
but it is known to millions of decimal places.
You will usually use one of these approximations:

$\pi = 3.1$ $\pi = 3.14$ $\pi = 3.142$ $\pi = \frac{22}{7}$ $\pi = 3\frac{1}{7}$

to 1 d.p.   to 2 d.p.   to 3 d.p.   as a   as a
                                     fraction   mixed number

Example 5

The radius of this circle is 14 cm.
Work out the circumference and area of the circle:

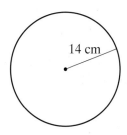

(a) using the approximation $\pi = \frac{22}{7}$

(b) leaving your answers in units of π.

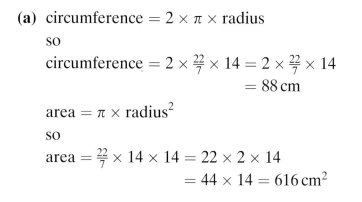

(a) circumference $= 2 \times \pi \times$ radius

so

circumference $= 2 \times \frac{22}{7} \times 14 = 2 \times \frac{22}{\cancel{7}} \times \cancel{14}$
$\qquad\qquad\qquad = 88$ cm

area $= \pi \times$ radius^2

so

area $= \frac{22}{7} \times 14 \times 14 = 22 \times 2 \times 14$
$\qquad\qquad\qquad = 44 \times 14 = 616$ cm^2

(b) circumference $= 2 \times \pi \times$ radius

so

circumference $= 2 \times \pi \times 14 = 28 \times \pi$
$\qquad\qquad\qquad\qquad = 28\pi$ cm (in units of π)

area $= \pi \times$ radius^2

so

area $= \pi \times 14^2 = \pi \times 196$
$\qquad\qquad = 196\pi$ cm^2 (in units of π)

Example 6

Look at this shape:

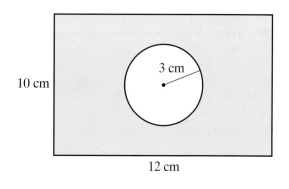

Using $\pi = 3.14$ work out:

(a) the circumference of the hole

(b) the area of the hole

(c) the area of the shaded shape.

(a) The circumference of the hole is:

$$\text{circumference} = 2\pi r$$
$$= 2 \times 3.14 \times 3$$
$$= 18.84 \text{ cm}$$

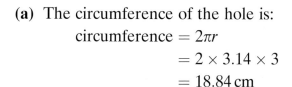

(b) The area of the hole is:

$$\begin{aligned} \text{area} &= \pi r^2 \\ &= 3.14 \times 3^2 \\ &= 28.26\,\text{cm}^2 \end{aligned}$$

(c) The area of the shaded region is the area of the rectangle take away the area of the hole:

$$\begin{aligned} \text{area of rectangle} &= \text{length} \times \text{width} \\ &= 10 \times 12 = 120\,\text{cm}^2 \\ \text{area of hole} \quad &= 28.26\,\text{cm}^2 \end{aligned}$$

So the area of the shaded region $= 120 - 28.26$
$$= 91.74\,\text{cm}^2$$

Exercise 15D

Unless told otherwise, use $\pi = 3.14$ in this exercise.

1 Work out the circumference and area of each of these circles. In each case use the approximation $\pi = \frac{22}{7}$.

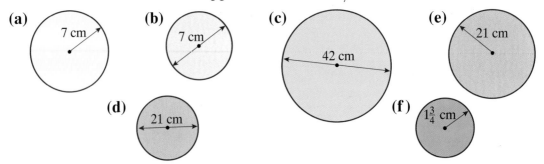

(a) 7 cm

(b) 7 cm

(c) 42 cm

(e) 21 cm

(d) 21 cm

(f) $1\frac{3}{4}$ cm

2 Work out the circumference and area of each of these circles. Leave all of your answers in units of π.

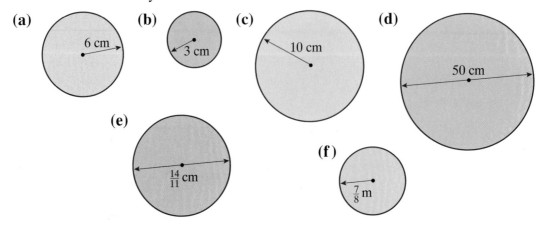

(a) 6 cm

(b) 3 cm

(c) 10 cm

(d) 50 cm

(e) $\frac{14}{11}$ cm

(f) $\frac{7}{8}$ m

3 Calculate the area of the shaded region

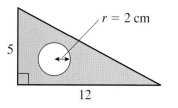

4 This diagram shows an athletics track.

Work out:

(a) the perimeter of the track

(b) the area inside the track.

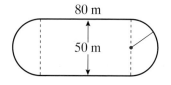

5 The circle and the square have equal areas.

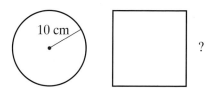

Work out the length of the square's sides to 2 decimal places.

6 This door is a rectangle with a semi-circular top.

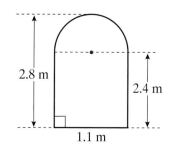

Work out:

(a) the perimeter of the door

(b) the area of the door.

7 Mrs Heath wants a new carpet for this floor. The carpet costs £8 per square metre. The skirting boards costs 40p per metre. Find the total cost of the carpet and skirting board.

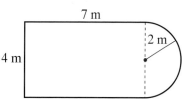

15.5 Volume and capacity

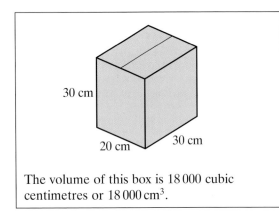

The volume of this box is 18 000 cubic centimetres or 18 000 cm³.

You can fit 18 000 centimetre cubes in the box. Its capacity is 18 000 cm³.

For hollow shapes with thin sides the volume is the same as the capacity.

■ **The volume is the amount of space that a shape takes up in three dimensions.**

■ **The amount of space inside a hollow three-dimensional shape is its capacity.**

The volume of a cuboid

You can find the volume of a cuboid by counting cubes:

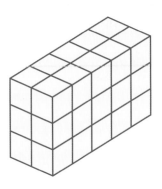 

Count the cubes. There are 30 so the volume is 30 cm³. But ...

... by thinking of the shape like this you can see that there are 3 rows of 2×5 cubes.
$3 \times 2 \times 5 = 30 \, \text{cm}^3$.

The area of the base of the shape is length × width.
The volume is area of base × height
$$= \text{length} \times \text{width} \times \text{height}$$

For any cuboid:

■ **Volume of a cuboid = length × width × height**

The volume of a cylinder

A cylinder is a prism with a circular base.

Its volume is area of base × height

For any cylinder

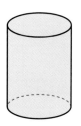

■ **Volume of a cylinder = π × radius^2 × height**

$$= \pi r^2 h$$

this is the area of the base

Example 7

Using $\pi = 3.14$ work out the volume of this cylinder.

Volume $= \pi r^2 h$

$= 3.14 \times 10^2 \times 15$

$= 3.14 \times 100 \times 15 = 4710\,\text{cm}^3$

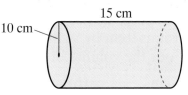

15 cm

10 cm

Exercise 15E

1   Work out the volume of each cuboid.

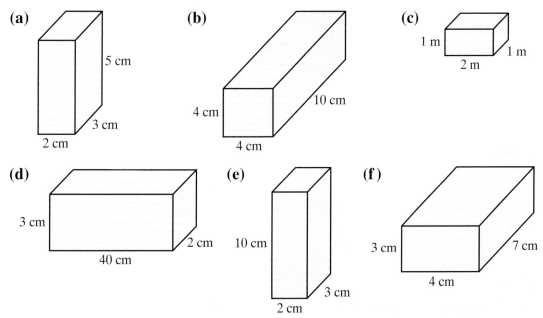

(a) 5 cm 3 cm 2 cm

(b) 4 cm 4 cm 10 cm

(c) 1 m 1 m 2 m

(d) 3 cm 40 cm 2 cm

(e) 10 cm 2 cm 3 cm

(f) 3 cm 4 cm 7 cm

2 Work out the volume of each cylinder.

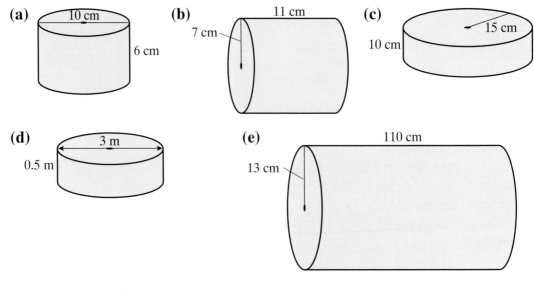

(a) 10 cm, 6 cm

(b) 11 cm, 7 cm

(c) 15 cm, 10 cm

(d) 3 m, 0.5 m

(e) 110 cm, 13 cm

3 This computer disk is a cuboid of dimensions 9 cm by 9 cm by 2 mm. Work out the volume of the disk:

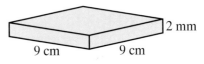

2 mm, 9 cm, 9 cm

(a) in cm³   **(b)** in mm³

4 A CD box is in the shape of a cuboid. It measures 14 cm by 12.5 cm by 8 mm. Work out the volume of the box in cm³.

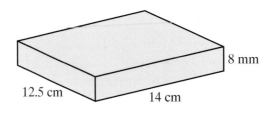

8 mm, 12.5 cm, 14 cm

5 A cylindrical can is made of very thin metal. The radius of the base is 5 cm. The height of the can is 30 cm. Work out the capacity of the can in:

(i) cm³   **(ii)** litres

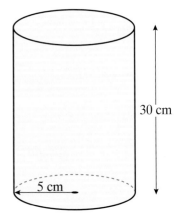

30 cm, 5 cm

6 Work out the capacity of this box:

(a) in cm^3

(b) in litres.

Hint:
1 litre = 1000 cm^3

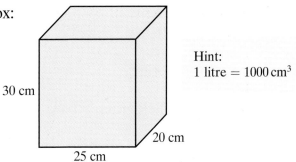

30 cm

25 cm

20 cm

7 Tom cuts some pieces of cheese into cuboids measuring 8 cm by 6 cm by 3 cm.
Work out the maximum number of these pieces of cheese which will fit into this box.

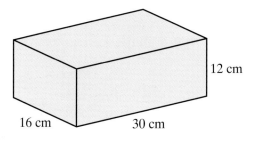

12 cm

16 cm

30 cm

8 Each domino is a cuboid measuring 5 cm by 2.5 cm by 8 mm.

(a) Work out the volume of each domino.

There are 28 dominoes in a full set.

(b) Design at least three cubical boxes which can contain a full set of dominoes. (The set of dominoes should make a tight fit in each box.)

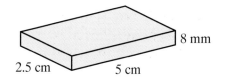

8 mm

2.5 cm

5 cm

Summary of key points

1 The distance around a flat shape is its perimeter.

2 The space covered by a flat shape is its area.

3 For any rectangle:
- Perimeter is $2 \times$ (length + width) or $2(l + w)$
- Its area is length $\times$ width or lw

4 Area of a triangle $= \frac{1}{2} \times$ base $\times$ height

5 Area of a trapezium $= \dfrac{(\text{base} + \text{top side})}{2} \times$ height

6 Area of a parallelogram $=$ base $\times$ height

7 Area of a kite $= \frac{1}{2} \times$ length $\times$ width

8 Circumference of a circle $= \pi \times$ diameter
$$= \pi \times 2 \times \text{radius or } 2\pi r$$

9 Area of a circle $= \pi \times \text{radius}^2$
$$= \pi r^2$$

10 Volume is the amount of space that a shape takes up in three dimensions.

11 Capacity is the amount of space inside a hollow three-dimensional shape.

12 Volume of a cuboid $=$ length $\times$ width $\times$ height

13 Volume of a cylinder $= \pi r^2 h$

16 Averages

■ **There are three types of mathematical average: the mode, median and mean.**

16.1 The mode

■ **The mode of a set of data is the value which occurs most often.**

Example 1

Saira was given a bunch of 10 flowers.
The colours of the flowers in the bunch were:

Red	White	Yellow	Red	Yellow
Blue	White	White	Pink	White

White is the colour which occurs most often here
so the **modal colour** is white.

When data is presented on a bar chart the mode can be spotted
easily by looking to see which value has the highest bar.

Example 2

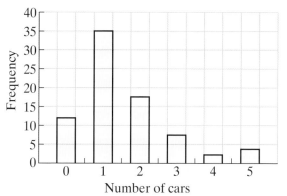

In a bar chart the mode is the value with the highest bar.

Here the mode is one car.

16.2 The median

- **The median is the middle value when the data is arranged in order of size.**

Example 3

Five children spent this much money last week:

£7   £15   £12   £10   £8

What is the median amount spent?

Arrange these amounts in order:

£7   £8   £10   £12   £15

The value in the middle is £10.
So the median amount of money spent last week was £10.

Sometimes a list can have an **even** number of values and there is no such thing as a middle value.

Example 4

There are eight people sharing the holiday caravan.
Their ages, in years and in order are

3   8   17   26   32   56   60   65

The **middle two** values are 26 and 32

The **median** value is

$$\frac{26 + 32}{2} = \frac{58}{2} = 29 \text{ years}$$

To find the median of an even number of values:

add the 2 middle values and divide by 2

16.3 The mean

- **The mean is the sum of all the values divided by the number of values:**

$$\text{Mean} = \frac{\text{sum of values}}{\text{number of values}}$$

Example 5

The numbers of wickets taken by the fast bowler in ten matches were

3   5   6   0   8   1   6   4   1   3

Work out the mean number of wickets taken per match.

$$\text{Mean} = \frac{3+5+6+0+8+1+6+4+1+3}{10} = \frac{37}{10} = 3.7$$

16.4 The range

■   **The range of a set of values is**
   largest value − smallest value

Example 6

The lowest temperature in Edinburgh was −5°C.
The range of the temperatures in Edinburgh was 28°C.

Work out the highest temperature in Edinburgh.

   highest − lowest = range

so   highest = lowest + range

so   highest temperature = −5 + 28 = 23°C.

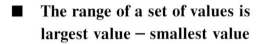

Exercise 16A

1   Calculate for each set of data:

   (a) the mode   **(b)** the median

   (c) the mean   **(d)** the range

   (i)   5, 3, 5, 7, 5, 1, 8, 9, 10, 2
   (ii) £12, £32, £15, £12, £30
   (iii) 1.8, 2.3, 5.6, 1.8, 3.5, 2.3, 4.5, 1.9, 2.7, 4.1

2 The number of house sales an estate agent makes per
month is shown in the table.

Month	Jan	Feb	Mar	Apr	May	Jun	Jly	Aug	Sep	Oct	Nov	Dec
Number of sales	8	12	23	15	20	12	25	12	21	18	15	12

Using the data, calculate:

(a) the mode   (b) the median   (c) the mean   (d) the range.

3 Ben throws a pair of dice 25 times. His scores are:

2, 7, 6, 8, 9, 10, 11, 3, 2,
5, 8, 6, 9, 12, 10, 8, 4, 3,
11, 12, 9, 10, 6, 7, 8

(a) Calculate the mean for the data.

(b) Calculate the median for the data.

(c) Calculate the mode for the data.

(d) Calculate the range for the data.

4 Here are Rehana and Sanam's English homework marks.

Rehana	70	60	70	71	71	69	61	69	68	71
Sanam	80	79	20	92	12	72	74	20	83	28

Copy and complete this table:

	Mode	Median	Mean	Range
Rehana				
Sanam				

5 The pupils in 8P did a science test. The highest mark
was 90%. The lowest mark was 48%.
Work out the range of the marks.

6 The youngest member of a gym is 14 years old. If the
range of ages of the members is 48 years, calculate the
age of the oldest member of the gym.

7 The range of mid-day temperatures in ten cities is 19°C.
The highest of these temperatures is 16°C.
Calculate the lowest of these temperatures.

16.5 Finding the mean from frequency tables

It is sometimes easier to use a frequency table to calculate the mean when there are many values.

$$\blacksquare \quad \text{mean} = \frac{\text{total of (each value} \times \text{frequency)}}{\text{total frequency}}$$

Example 7

This table shows the number of books pupils in 8P borrowed from the school library one week.

Number of books	Frequency
0	1
1	2
2	4
3	5
4	7
5	10
6	3

This means 4 pupils borrowed 2 books

$$\text{mean} = \frac{\text{total number of books}}{\text{total frequency}}$$

Re-draw the table to find the total number of children:

Number of books	Frequency	Number of books × frequency
0	1	$0 \times 1 = 0$
1	2	$1 \times 2 = 2$
2	4	$2 \times 4 = 8$
3	5	$3 \times 5 = 15$
4	7	$4 \times 7 = 28$
5	10	$5 \times 10 = 50$
6	3	$6 \times 3 = 18$
total frequency = 32		total number of books $= 121$

This tells us the total number of pupils

$$\text{mean} = \frac{\text{total number of books}}{\text{total frequency}} = \frac{121}{32}$$

mean = 3.78 correct to 2 decimal places.

So the mean number of books borrowed per pupil is 3.78.

Exercise 16B

1 The number of games a player wins in 200 sets of tennis is shown in this bar chart.

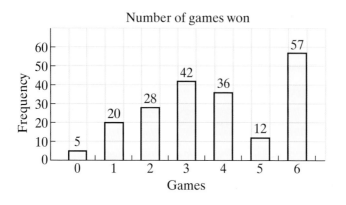

Number of games won

(a) Draw a frequency table for the data.

(b) Work out the mean number of games the player wins in a set.

2 This table shows the number of passengers travelling in taxis.

Number of passengers	Frequency	Number of passengers × frequency
0	23	0 × 23 = 0
1		1 × = 22
2	34	2 × 34 = 68
3	20	3 × 20 =
4	55	4 × 55 = 220
5		5 × =
total frequency = 200		total number of passengers = 600

The mean is 3 passengers.

Copy this table and fill in the missing numbers.

16.6 Finding the median from a frequency table

Sometimes you need to find the median from a frequency table.

Example 8

This table shows how many homeworks per night Jo got last term.

Number of homeworks	Frequency
1	13
2	34
3	22
4	6

on 6 nights Jo got 4 homeworks

To find the median add a **cumulative frequency** column to the table.

■ **The cumulative frequency is the running total of the frequencies.**

Number of homeworks	Frequency	Cumulative frequency
1	13	13
2	34	47
3	22	69
4	6	75

Here the running total is
$13 + 34 + 22 = 69$

Jo got 75 homeworks altogether last term

The median is the middle value:

$$\text{median} = \frac{75 + 1}{2} = \frac{76}{2} = 38$$

so the median is the 38th value.

To find the middle value add 1 to the total number of values, then divide the result by 2.

Number of homeworks	Frequency	Cumulative frequency
1	13	13
2	34	47
3	22	69
4	6	75

The 14th to the 47th values are all 2.

So the median is 2 homeworks.

■ **The median is the value half-way along the cumulative frequency.**

Example 9

The number of times John has to dial before he gets through to his friend is shown in the table.

Number of times John dials	Frequency
1	14
2	6
3	5
4	7
5	5
6	3

Find the median of this data.

Redraw the table with the cumulative frequency column.

Number of times John dials	Frequency	Cumulative frequency	
1	14	14	
2	6	20	—— 20th value is 2
3	5	25	—— 21st value is 3
4	7	32	
5	5	37	
6	3	40	

$$\text{The median value} = \frac{\text{total number of values} + 1}{2}$$

$$= \frac{40 + 1}{2}$$

$$= 20\tfrac{1}{2}\text{th value}$$

To find the $20\tfrac{1}{2}$th value you have to add the 20th and 21st values and divide the result by 2:

$$\frac{2 + 3}{2} = 2\tfrac{1}{2}$$

So the median number of times John dials is $2\tfrac{1}{2}$.

Exercise 16C

1 Levi goes to judo class. She won her blackbelt when she was 12.
This table shows how many other blackbelts there are in Levi's class:

Age	Frequency
11	5
12	3
13	10
14	5
15	9
16	6

Calculate the median age.

2 The table shows the frequency table for the number of students cycling into school each day.

Number of pupils who cycle	Frequency
0	15
1	28
2	50
3	41
4	34
5	27
6	5

Calculate the median.

3 This graph shows the number of callouts a lifeboat answers each week during two years.

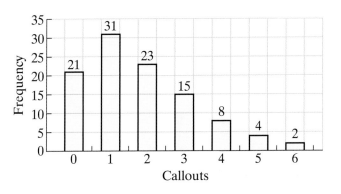

(a) Use the graph to complete this frequency table:

Number of callouts	Frequency
0	
1	
2	
3	
4	
5	
6	

(b) Work out the median.

4 This table shows the results for a mental maths test.

The marks are out of 10.

Mark	0	1	2	3	4	5	6	7	8	9	10
Frequency	0	0	1	2	2	0	9	8	4	4	3

Calculate

(a) the median

(b) the mean

(c) the mode.

16.7 Using appropriate averages

The three different averages are the mode, median and mean.

Sometimes you need to know which type of average is best to use.

The mode is useful when you need to know things like:

"what is most people's favourite colour?"

"which holiday destination is most popular?"

The median is useful for finding a 'typical' value if the data is very spread out. For example:

"what is the average height for a pupil in your class?"

If the data is not very spread out, the mean may provide a more 'typical' value. For example:

"what is a typical price for one of these scientific calculators?"

Example 10

The number of veggie whoppers served by the canteen last half-term was:

wk 1	wk 2	wk 3	wk 4	wk 5	wk 6	wk 7	wk 8
39	51	43	30	43	4	7	3

Find the mode, median and mean number of veggie whoppers sold.

Comment on your results.

The mode is 43 veggie whoppers.

The median is the middle value:

51   43   43   39   30   7   4   3

2 middle values

so median $= \dfrac{39 + 30}{2} = 34.5$

The mean number of veggie whoppers is:

$$\frac{51 + 43 + 43 + 39 + 30 + 7 + 4 + 3}{8} = \frac{220}{8} = 27.5$$

so the mode is 43, median 34.5 and the mean is 27.5.

Here the median gives us the best idea of a typical number of veggie whoppers sold. Half the sales are more than this and half are less.

The mode is not representative as only one sale is higher.

The mean has been distorted by the three very low sales.

Exercise 16D

1 This table shows the temperature in August for two resorts.

Resort	Sixby	Torcliffe
Mean temperature	23°C	26°C
Range	5°C	10°C

Which resort would you prefer?
Give a reason for your answer.

2 This table shows data for runs scored per innings by Alan, Carol and Phillip over one season.

Cricketer	Alan	Carol	Phillip
Mean score	23	34	50
Range	5	10	31

Which player do you think is best at cricket?
Give a reason for your answer.

3 Here are Craig's art homework marks during last term:

5	7	8	4	2	6	1	3	8	9	10	8	10

(a) Work out the mean, mode and median of his marks.

(b) Which average is lowest?

4 This table shows the number of merits gained per week by 8C.

Number of merits	Frequency
10	11
11	10
12	5
13	3
14	4
15	3
16	3

this means 8C got 12 merits during 5 weeks

(a) Work out the mean, mode and median for the number of merits.

(b) Which average should 8C use?

5 There are 10 houses in Markfield Avenue. The number of letters they each receive one Monday are recorded below.

House number	1	2	3	4	5	6	7	8	9	10
Number of letters	2	1	0	2	3	30	1	1	0	1

(a) Work out the mean number of letters received.

(b) Explain why the mean is not a sensible average to use in this case.

(c) Give, with justification, another average.

6 Give an example when you might sensibly wish to use

(a) the mode as a measure of average

(b) the median as a measure of average

(c) the mean as a measure of average.

7 George is aged 54.
His daughter Sally is aged 16.
'The average of their ages is 35.'
Comment on this statement.

8 A group of ten pupils took a spelling test marked out of 20.
Five of the pupils were girls and five of the pupils were boys.

The results in the test are shown below.

Girls   8   9   10   11   12
Boys   13   0   13   1   13

(a) Work out the mode, median, mean and range for each of these sets of results.

(b) Does the evidence support the comment that the girls have, on average, done better in the spelling test than the boys? Please explain your answer.

9 The police conducted a survey of the speeds of traffic using the M1 and the A1 at 6 am one morning.

The results of the survey were:

A1   Mean speed 65 miles per hour   Range of speeds 15 miles per hour
M1   Mean speed 60 miles per hour   Range of speeds 30 miles per hour

A newspaper comments that cars tend to travel faster on the A1 than they do on the M1.

Do you agree with the newspaper comment? Say why.

Summary of key points

1 There are three types of mathematical average:
the mode, median and mean.

2 The mode of a set of data is the value which occurs most often.

3 The median is the middle value when the data is arranged in order of size.

4 The mean is the sum of all the values divided by the number of values:

$$\text{Mean} = \frac{\text{sum of values}}{\text{number of values}}$$

5 The range of a set of values is
largest value – smallest value

6 When using a frequency table:

$$\text{mean} = \frac{\text{total of (each value} \times \text{frequency)}}{\text{total frequency}}$$

7 The cumulative frequency is the running total of the frequencies.

8 The median is the value half-way along the cumulative frequency.

17 Using and applying mathematics

In this chapter you will learn about the process behind doing a mathematical investigation.

This is the problem that you will be investigating:

Shaking hands

Andrea has a birthday party:

She asks each of her friends to shake hands with everyone else just once.

Investigate to find the relationship between the number of friends and the number of handshakes.

The first step is to:

Understand the problem

The best way to understand the problem is to just have a go. Suppose Andrea has invited four friends: Bronwen, Charlie, Dipesh and Elaine.

Five of the possible handshakes could be:

Andrea and Bronwen
Andrea and Charlie
Andrea and Dipesh
Andrea and Elaine
Bronwen and Charlie

Exercise 17A

1   Find the other five handshakes to show that there are ten possible handshakes when there are four friends.

Make the problem as simple as you can

To help you understand the problem, try out the simplest cases first.

Example 1

How many handshakes will there be if Andrea invites one friend, Bronwen?

There will be one handshake:

Andrea and Bronwen

Example 2

How many handshakes will there be if Andrea invites Charlie as well, so there are two friends?

The handshakes will be:

Andrea and Bronwen
Andrea and Charlie
Bronwen and Charlie

So there will be three handshakes if Andrea invites two friends

Exercise 17B

1   List all the handshakes if Andrea invites three friends: Bronwen, Charlie and Dipesh.

How many handshakes are there with three friends?

Plan and use a strategy

A strategy is an ordered approach to a problem.

Imagine trying to work out how many handshakes there would be at this party!

Using a strategy will mean that you don't miss any handshakes.

Example 3

How many handshakes will there be if Andrea invites five friends: Bronwen, Charlie, Dipesh, Elaine and Flora?

The strategy will be:

Count all of Andrea's handshakes first.
Then count all of Bronwen's.
Then count all of Charlie's.
And so on . . .
To save time just use the first letter of each name:
AF = Andrea and Flora
The handshakes for each person are:

Andrea: AB   AC   AD   AE   AF   5
Bronwen: BC   BD   BE   BF   4
Charlie: CD   CE   CF   3
Dipesh: DE   DF   2
Elaine: EF   1

Flora has already shaken hands with everyone.

So the number of handshakes for 5 friends is:

$$5 + 4 + 3 + 2 + 1 = 15$$

Hint:
You don't need to do BA as Bronwen has already shaken hands with Andrea.

Exercise 17C

1   (a) Use this strategy to check the results so far:

Number of friends: 1   2   3   4   5

Number of handshakes: 1   3   6   10   15

(b) Use the strategy to show that there will be 21 handshakes if Andrea invites a sixth friend, Graham.

Record your results

Once you have started to get some results it is best to record them in a table.

1   Copy and complete this table:

Number of friends	Number of handshakes
1	1
2	3
3	6
6	

Always make sure your tables are clearly labelled.

Make predictions

Once you have your results in a table you should see if you can find any patterns.

A simple pattern to see here is that the number of handshakes grows as the number of friends grows.

The number of handshakes also follows a pattern:

1	3	6	10	15	21
odd	odd	even	even	odd	odd

which is not so obvious.

You can use your observations to make **predictions**.

Example 4

Predict whether the number of handshakes will be odd or even for seven friends.

The results so far are:

Number of friends	Number of handshakes	Odd or even
1	1	odd
2	3	odd
3	6	even
4	10	even
5	15	odd
6	21	odd
7		even

Even though you don't know the number of handshakes you can predict that it will be an even number.

Exercise 17E

1   Predict whether there will be an odd or even number when there are:

   (a) 10 friends   **(b)** 20 friends   **(c)** 50 friends

   Show how you get your answers.

A good way to find patterns in number sequences is to use **differences**. You can see a pattern in your results if you find the difference between each pair of numbers.

Number of friends	1	2	3	4	5	6
Number of handshakes	1	3	6	10	15	21

$$+2 \quad +3 \quad +4 \quad +5 \quad +6$$

The number of handshakes increases by a simple pattern   2, 3, 4, 5, 6, ...

You can use this to predict that for 7 friends there will be $21 + 7 = 28$ handshakes.

Example 5

How many handshakes will there be for 8 friends?

Use the pattern to make a prediction:

```
   +2   +3   +4   +5   +6   +7   +8
  ⌒    ⌒    ⌒    ⌒    ⌒    ⌒    ⌒
 1    3    6    10   15   21   28   36 handshakes
```

If you know the pattern and the first answer you can find the answer without drawing out the whole table each time.

Exercise 17F

1   Use a pattern to predict how many handshakes there will be for:

    (a) 8 friends   **(b)** 9 friends   **(c)** 10 friends

Testing predictions

Whenever you make a prediction you should test it to check whether it is a good one.

Example 6

Test the prediction that there will be 28 handshakes if Andrea invites 7 friends.

Use the strategy to count the handshakes.

```
Andrea:    AB  AC  AD  AE  AF  AG  AH
Bronwen:   BC  BD  BE  BF  BG  BH
Charlie:   CD  CE  CF  CG  CH
Dipesh:    DE  DF  DG  DH
Elaine:    EF  EG  EH
Flora:     FG  FH
Graham:    GH
```
Herbert has already shaken hands with everyone.

There are 28 pairs of letters so there are 28 handshakes when Andrea invites 7 friends.
The prediction was a good one!

Exercise 17G

1 Using the strategy, test the predictions that you made for:
   (a) 8 friends   **(b)** 9 friends   **(c)** 10 friends

Making a generalization

Once you have tested a prediction you can make a
generalization. You can make some generalizations about
shaking hands:

- The bigger the number of friends the bigger the
  number of handshakes.
- The number of handshakes follows the pattern odd,
  odd, even, even.
- You can find the number of handshakes by finding
  $1 + 2 + 3 + 4 + 5 + \ldots$
  stopping at the number of friends invited to the party.

The last generalization means that you can work out the
number of handshakes just by knowing the number of
friends invited.

You may also have noticed that there is a pattern to the
answers. Look at the answers up to four friends:

One friend:
Andrea: AB
Bronwen:

Two friends:
Andrea: AB   AC
Bronwen: BC
Charlie:

Three friends:
Andrea: AB   AC   AD
Bronwen: BC   BD
Charlie: CD
Dipesh:

Remember:
The last friend has
already shaken hands
with everyone.

Four friends:

Andrea: AB   AC   AD   AE

Bronwen: BC   BD   BE

Charlie: CD   CE

Dipesh: DE

Elaine:

The number of handshakes forms a triangular pattern.
The numbers 1, 3, 6, 10, 15 ... are called the **triangular numbers**.

Triangular number	1st	2nd	3rd	4th	5th
Value	1	3	6	10	15
Pattern	•	• • •	• • • • • •	• • • • • • • • • •	• • • • • • • • • • • • • • •

So any generalization about the number of handshakes is a
generalization about triangular numbers and vice versa.

Look at the pattern for the
4th triangular number, 10:

You can repeat the triangle upside
down to make this rectangle:

The number of dots in the rectangle is:

$$4 \times 5 = 20$$

The rectangle is made from two equal triangles so divide by
two:

$$\tfrac{1}{2} \times 20 = 10$$

which is the 4th triangular number.

Example 7

Show that the 3rd triangular number is $\dfrac{3 \times 4}{2}$.

The dot pattern is: Make the rectangle:

The rectangle has $3 \times 4 = 12$ dots, so

the 3rd triangular number $= \dfrac{3 \times 4}{2} = 6$.

Exercise 17H

1   Show that:

    (a) the fifth triangular number $= \dfrac{5 \times 6}{2}$

    (b) the sixth triangular number $= \dfrac{6 \times 7}{2}$

Try to make a generalization from your results:

1st triangular number $= \dfrac{1 \times 2}{2}$

2nd triangular number $= \dfrac{2 \times 3}{2}$

3rd triangular number $= \dfrac{3 \times 4}{2}$

4th triangular number $= \dfrac{4 \times 5}{2}$

As the number of handshakes follows the pattern for the triangular numbers you can predict a rule:

Number of handshakes $= \dfrac{\text{number of friends} \times (\text{number of friends} + 1)}{2}$

Exercise 17I

1 Use this rule to check your earlier answers for

(**a**) 5 friends   (**b**) 6 friends   (**c**) 7 friends

(**d**) 8 friends   (**e**) 9 friends   (**f**) 10 friends

The predicted rule works so you have a generalization that lets you work out the number of handshakes without having to add $1 + 2 + 3 + 4 + 5 + \ldots$

A running commentary

Throughout your investigation you should give reasons for all the decisions you made. You should also consider different ways of presenting your work such as in a table or as a graph. Explain why you chose that style to present your results. Look for evidence that will back up any ideas you have had that worked or any patterns you might have spotted.

Trying out some investigations

Here are some investigations to help you practise recording your results, looking for patterns, testing your predictions and making generalizations.

Exercise 17J

1 Beth is painting the outside of this cube red.

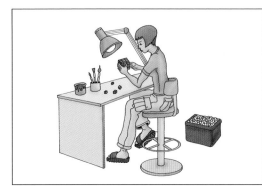
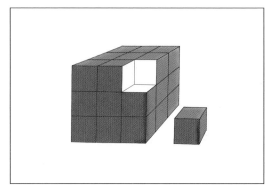

After the paint has dried, Beth takes the cube apart.
She notices that different cubes have different numbers
of faces painted red.

Some have three faces painted red:

Some others have two faces painted red:

Some have only one red face:

and one had no red faces!

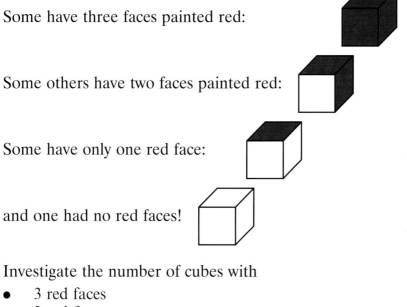

Investigate the number of cubes with
- 3 red faces
- 2 red faces
- 1 red face
- no red faces

Could Beth make
- a smaller cube?
- larger cubes?

Investigate, using different sizes of cubes.

Summary of key points

The steps you should take in any mathematical
investigation are:

- Understand the problem – have a go.
- Make the problem as simple as you can.
- Use an ordered approach – plan a strategy.
- Record your results – make a table.
- Make predictions.
- Test your predictions.
- Try to make a generalization.

18 Calculators and computers

This chapter shows you ways of using scientific calculators, graphical calculators and computer software. The examples will work on Casio calculators, the spreadsheet examples are based on Microsoft Excel and the examples for drawing angles, polygons and triangles work with WinLogo.

18.1 Using your square root key

You can find square roots using the key

Example 1

Find   **(a)** $\sqrt{25}$ **(b)** $\sqrt{4} + \sqrt{9}$ **(c)** $\sqrt{(3^2 + 4^2)}$

(a) Press:

Answer: 5

(b) Press:

Answer: 5

(c) Press:

Answer: 5

> On some earlier models of calculator you enter the number before pressing the √ key:
>
> 2 5 √
>
> Answer 5:
>
> Some calculators have only one key for square roots and squares. Check whether you need to press the SHIFT key before the
>
> √ or x^2
>
> Get to know your calculator!

Exercise 18A   Scientific calculator

1 Calculate $\sqrt{324}$

2 Calculate $\sqrt{1369}$

3 Calculate $\sqrt{576}$

4 Calculate $\sqrt{2304} - \sqrt{289}$

5 Calculate $\sqrt{(6^2 + 8^2)}$

6 Calculate $\sqrt{(5^2 + 12^2)}$

7 Calculate $\sqrt{25} + \sqrt{144}$

8 Calculate $\sqrt{441} \div \sqrt{49}$

9 Calculate $\sqrt{1521} \div \sqrt{169}$

10 Investigate what happens if you keep taking the square root starting with any 10 digit number.

11 Use square numbers for *a* and *b* to investigate whether

(a) $\sqrt{(a \times b)} = \sqrt{a} \times \sqrt{b}$ **(b)** $\sqrt{(a + b)} = \sqrt{a} + \sqrt{b}$
(c) $\sqrt{(a \div b)} = \sqrt{a} \div \sqrt{b}$ **(d)** $\sqrt{(a - b)} = \sqrt{a} - \sqrt{b}$

Press the $\boxed{\sqrt{\ }}$ key,

enter your 10 digit number, press

18.2 Using your powers key

You can calculate the value of numbers like 3^5 using the $\boxed{x^y}$ key.

3^5 is shorthand for
$3 \times 3 \times 3 \times 3 \times 3$
You say '3 to the power of 5'.

There is more about powers on page 5.

Example 2

Find   **(a)** 3^5 **(b)** $4^3 + 9^4$ **(c)** $8^6 \div 2^4$

(a) Press:

$\boxed{3}\ \boxed{x^y}\ \boxed{5}\ \boxed{=}$

Answer: 243

(b) Press:

$\boxed{4}\ \boxed{x^y}\ \boxed{3}\ \boxed{+}\ \boxed{9}\ \boxed{x^y}\ \boxed{4}\ \boxed{=}$

Answer: 6625

(c) Press:

$\boxed{8}\ \boxed{x^y}\ \boxed{6}\ \boxed{\div}\ \boxed{2}\ \boxed{x^y}\ \boxed{4}\ \boxed{=}$

Answer: 16 384

Exercise 18B   Scientific calculator

1 Calculate:

(a) 6^3 **(b)** 8^7
(c) $10^3 + 10^5$ **(d)** $6^8 \div 3^5$

2 **(a)** Which is bigger 2^{30} or 3^{20}?

   (b) By how much?

3 Calculate:

   (a) $(2^3)^4$

   (b) $(2^4)^3$

   (c) $(4^3)^2$

4 If n is a positive whole number what is the *smallest* value of n which makes 4^n bigger than 5^{12}?

5 **(a)** Calculate 100^1

   (b) Calculate $1^{1^{1^{\cdots}}}$

   (c) Calculate a^0, where a is any positive whole number.

6 **(a)** In the book **One Grain of Rice: A Mathematical Folktale** by Demi (Illustrator), a young woman called Rani outwitted the Raja to gain food for her starving people. Rani demanded that she be given 1 grain of rice on day 1 and each day after for a total of thirty days the number of grains of rice given should be doubled. Calculate the total number of grains of rice Rani obtained for her people.

   The total rice is

   $1 + 2 + 4 + 8 + 16 + \ldots$

   or, in power notation,

   $2^0 + 2^1 + 2^2 + 2^3 + 2^4 + \ldots + 2^{29}$

   (b) A packet of rice contains approximately $17\,000$ grains. Approximately how many packets would be required to obtain the equivalent amount of rice in modern times?

7 What do you notice about the digits in the questions and answers if you calculate

   (a) $3^3 + 4^4 + 3^3 + 5^5$

   (b) $88^2 + 33^2$

   (c) $4^4 + 3^3 + 8^8 + 5^5 + 7^7 + 9^9 + 0^0 + 8^8 + 8^8$

   (d) 567^2

   (e) 854^2

   Entering 0^0 on your calculator may give an error. Enter 0 instead.

8 For $n = 1$ to 10, which of $2^n - 1$ are prime numbers?

There is more about prime numbers on page 3.

18.3 Generating sequences

You can use a spreadsheet to generate sequences.
To work out a formula in a spreadsheet:

There is more on
sequences on
page 147.

Enter the first term in the top row:

	A	B
1	12	
2		
3		
4		

Enter the formula to generate the next term:

	A	B
1	12	
2	=A1+1	
3		
4		

Click and drag this black square down to generate more terms:

	A	B
1	12	
2	13	
3		
4		

Exercise 18C   Spreadsheet

1 Use this process to generate the first 30 terms in each of these sequences:

	A	B	C	D	E	F	G
1	12	40	4	−6	−6	1	1
2	13	38	8	−3	−9	3	2
3	14	36	16	0	−12	7	5
4	15	34	32	3	−15	15	14

2 The polygonal numbers are the complete set of numbers which extend the triangular numbers and square numbers.

There is more on
triangular numbers
on page 290 and
on square numbers
on page 5.

The formula to generate the pentagonal numbers is $\frac{1}{2}n(3n - 1)$, where $n = 1, 2, 3, 4, \ldots$

If $n = 1$ the formula gives:
$$\tfrac{1}{2}(1)(3 \times 1 - 1) = 1$$

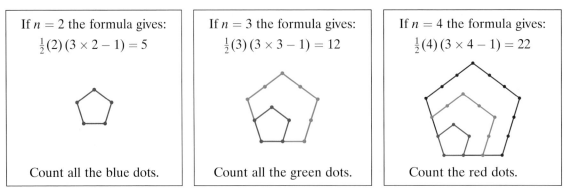

If $n = 2$ the formula gives: $\frac{1}{2}(2)(3 \times 2 - 1) = 5$	If $n = 3$ the formula gives: $\frac{1}{2}(3)(3 \times 3 - 1) = 12$	If $n = 4$ the formula gives: $\frac{1}{2}(4)(3 \times 4 - 1) = 22$
Count all the blue dots.	Count all the green dots.	Count the red dots.

The table below shows some of the other formulae:

Name	Formula
Triangular	$\frac{1}{2}(n)(n + 1)$
Square	$\frac{1}{2}(n)(2n - 0)$
Pentagonal	$\frac{1}{2}(n)(3n - 1)$
Hexagonal	$\frac{1}{2}(n)(4n - 2)$
Heptagonal	
Octagonal	

and so on …

(a) Follow the pattern in the table to produce the formulae needed to generate

- the heptagonal numbers
- the octagonal numbers.

(b) Use a spreadsheet to generate the first 30 terms for each type of sequence in the table.

	A	B	C	D	E
1	Term in sequence	Triangular numbers	Square numbers	Pentagonal numbers	Hexagonal numbers
2	1	1	1	1	1
3	2	3	4	5	6
4	3	6	9	12	15
5	4	10	16	22	28

Use column A to generate each of the sequences.

(c) Look for patterns in the rows and use formulae to extend the numbers horizontally.

3 Why is it not possible to use a spreadsheet to generate the first 100 prime numbers?

18.4 **Percentage increase and decrease**

> Page 102 shows you how to increase and decrease by a percentage.
>
> Here is another method:
>
> - To **increase** by 8% multiply by 1.08 [1 + 0.08]
> - To **decrease** by 8% multiply by 0.92 [1 − 0.08]

Example 3

(a) Increase £350 by 8%   (b) Decrease £650 by 8%

(c) Increase 70 kg by 14%   (d) Decrease $4.56 by 16.5%

(a) Press:

3 5 0 × 1 · 0 8

Answer: £378

(b) Press:

6 5 0 × · 9 2

Answer: £598

(c) Press:

7 0 × 1 · 1 4

Answer: 79.8 kg

$1 - 0.165 = 0.835$

(d) Press:

4 · 5 6 × · 8 3 5

Answer: $3.8076 or $3.81 to the nearest cent.

Exercise 18D   Scientific calculator

1 A computer was reduced in a sale by 12%. Before the sale the computer was priced at £2650. What was its sale price?

2 Last year Matthew weighed 65.4 kg and his height was 1.65 m. During this year his weight has increased by 2% and his height by 3.5%. Calculate his present weight and present height, to the nearest centimetre.

3 Ali was earning £26 500 a year when he was given an increase of 3%. What is his new salary?

4 In the 1998/1999 soccer season the average home attendance for a team was 32 456. The following season this increased by 7%. What was the new average attendance?

5 Anna-Natasha put £3658 in a Building Society. Each year her money increased by 6%. How much money, to the nearest penny, has Anna-Natasha in her account after:

(a) 1 year   (b) 2 years   (c) 5 years?

6 Joshua went into his local games store and bought 2 light guns at £14.99 each, 5 CD-R games at £17.99 each, 1 dual shock analogue joy pad at £18.99 each, 6 memory cards at £10.95 each and 2 scart cables for £7.98 each. If 17.5% VAT was added to the total, what was Joshua's final bill?

Remember to press the equals sign before calculating the VAT.

There is more on VAT on page 108.

18.5 Number machines

You can use a spreadsheet to find the output of a number machine.

There is more on number machines on page 149.

Example 4

This is a × 0.8 number machine:

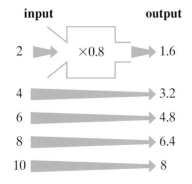

To produce the inputs and outputs above:

Enter 2 in cell A1 and the two formulae in cells A2 and B1.

	A	B
1	2	=A1*0.8
2	=A1+2	
3		
4		
5		

Copy down the formula in cell A2 to A5 and the formula in B1 to B5.

	A	B
1	2	=A1*0.8
2	=A1+2	=A2*0.8
3	=A2+2	=A3*0.8
4	=A3+2	=A4*0.8
5	=A4+2	=A5*0.8

This will produce the required inputs and outputs in column A and column B.

	A	B
1	2	1.6
2	4	3.2
3	6	4.8
4	8	6.4
5	10	8

Exercise 18E   Spreadsheet

1 Use a spreadsheet to create the inputs and outputs for these number machines:

Remember to work out the rule for the input column so that you can enter that formula in your spreadsheet. The formula for the output column comes from the given rule.

(a)

input	rule	output
3	× 0.6	
6		
9		
12		
15		

(b)

input	rule	output
12	÷ 0.8	
10		
8		
6		
4		

(c)

input	rule	output
5	increase by 5%	
10		
15		
20		
25		

(d)

input	rule	output
10000	decrease by 12%	
2000		
400		
80		
16		

2 Use the inputs in Question **1(a)** and the rule 'multiply by 3 and then subtract 4'.

3 Use the inputs in Question **1(a)** and the rule 'subtract 4 and then multiply by 4'.

4 Use the inputs in Question **1(b)** and the rule 'multiply by 1.6 and then divide by 1.6'.

5 Use the inputs in Question **1(c)** and the rule 'increase by 10% and then decrease by 10%'.

In questions 2 to 5 use three columns:
- input
- first output
- second output

18.6 Handling data

You can use a spreadsheet to calculate the mean, median, mode and range for given data.

Exercise 18F   Spreadsheet

1 **(a)** Enter the following data in cells A1 to A10 on a spreadsheet

        3, 5, 7, 12, 17, 17, 22, 26, 27, 85

    (b) In cell A11 enter a formula to calculate the mean average of the data

    (c) In cell A12 enter a formula to calculate the median average of the data

    (d) In cell A13 enter a formula to calculate the mode of the data

    (e) In cell A14 enter a formula to calculate the range of the data

    (f) Which is the fairest type of average? Give reasons for your choice.

2 Repeat steps **(a)** to **(f)** above in columns B to D. Make:

    (a) column B the original data multiplied by 10

    (b) column C original data plus 3

    (c) column D 5 times the original data plus 2.

    (d) Comment on your answers.

3 Use the data on extreme weather conditions given in the table on the following page to create a scatter graph on a spreadsheet:

    (a) the number of millimetres of rain against the number of minutes of rainfall

    (b) the number of millimetres of rain against the date of the month.

    (c) Comment on the type of correlation for each graph, giving reasons.

In Microsoft Excel the formulae are

- =average (A1:A10) to calculate the mean
- =median (A1:A10) to calculate the median
- =mode (A1:A10) to calculate the mode
- =A10–A1 to give the range

There is more about averages on page 269.

Here the data is ten times bigger than the original data. Will the averages be 10 times bigger?

Use the chart wizard in Excel to create graphs.

Intense rainfall in minutes (UK)

Minutes	mm	LOCATION	Date	Month	Year
5	32	Preston (Lancashire)	10	AUG	1893
12	51	Wisbech (Cambridgeshire)	27	JUN	1970
15	56	Bolton (Greater Manchester)	18	JUL	1964
20	63	Sidcup (Kent)	5	SEP	1958
20	63	Hindolveston (Norfolk)	11	JUL	1959
25	67	Pershore (Worcestershire)	11	JUN	1970
30	80	Eskdalemuir (Dumfries)	26	JUN	1953
45	97	Orra Beg (Antrim)	1	AUG	1980
60	92	Maidenhead (Berkshire)	12	JUL	1901
75	102	Wisley (Surrey)	16	JUL	1947
75	95	Ilkley (North Yorkshire)	12	JUL	1900
90	117	Dunsop Valley (Lancashire)	8	AUG	1967
90	111	Miserden (Gloucestershire)	10	JUN	1970
100	116	West Wickham (London)	22	JUL	1934
105	116	Sevenoaks (Kent)	25	JUN	1980
120	131	Knockholt (Kent)	5	SEP	1958
120	155	Hewenden Reservoir (Yorkshire)	11	JUN	1956
120	193	Walshaw Dean Lodge (Yorkshire)	19	MAY	1989
155	169	Hampstead (London)	14	AUG	1975
180	178	Horncastle (Lincolnshire)	7	OCT	1960

18.7 Angles and polygons

You can draw angles, triangles and polygons on a computer using the program WinLogo.

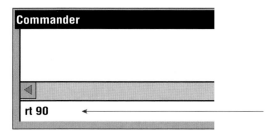

Type your instructions here and then press the Enter key before typing your next instruction.

In WinLogo you must provide instructions to move the 'turtle' around the screen.

The turtle begins this way round

`rt 90`
will turn it
90° clockwise

`fd 100`
will move it forward
'100' places and draw a
line '100' units long

Example 5

Draw on screen

(a) an angle of 110°

(b) an acute angle

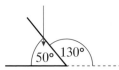

(a) Type
  rt 90
  fd 100
  lt 70
  fd 100

(b) Type
  rt 90
  fd 100
  lt 130
  fd 100

To draw an obtuse angle, you need to turn through an angle less than 90° and anticlockwise.
Type lt 70:

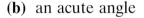

now move the turtle forward '100' units again.
fd 100

Exercise 18G

1 Use WinLogo to draw

  (a) an angle of 165°

  (b) an angle of 50°

  (c) an angle of 215°

  (d) a right-angle

  (e) an equilateral triangle of side 110 units

  (f) a square of side 150 units

  (g) a regular hexagon of side 140 units

  (h) a regular octagon of side 100 units

  (i) a circle

  (j) a tessellation pattern

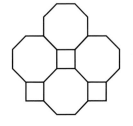

Hint:
Plan the shapes on paper first.

A quick way to draw the square in part **(f)** is to type
repeat 4 [fd 150 rt 90]

Think of a circle as a polygon with a lot of short sides!

A tessellation pattern is when polygons fit together with no gaps between them.

18.8 Creating some common shapes

You can use WinLogo to create shapes you can use more than once. To do this you must write a **procedure** in the WinLogo editor.

To create a procedure called *rectangle1*:

```
Commander



◁

edit"rectangle1
```

Type this instruction to bring up the Editor

```
  Editor
 File   Edit   Search   Set   Test!   Help
to rectangle1
repeat 2[fd 40 rt 90 fd 20 rt 90]
end
```

Add this code needed to produce a 20 by 40 unit rectangle and then click File and Exit to save the procedure and leave the Editor

In the Commander type and enter **rectangle1** and the turtle will draw the rectangle.

Exercise 18H   WinLogo

1   Write procedures to produce the following shapes:

Shape	Size	Procedure name
Rectangle	40 / 20	rectangle2
Square	40 units square	square1
Flag		flag1
Flag		flag2

Call your procedures: rectangle2, square1, flag1 and flag2 and save them in your area for future use

```
Save As
 File name:
 shapes1.lgo
```

18.9 Straight lines

You can draw lines on a graphical calculator. After you have switched on the calculator select the **GRAPH** icon using the arrow keys and then press the EXE key to display a window similar to

```
G-Func  :Y=
Y1:
Y2:
Y3:
Y4:
SEL DEL          DRAW
```

Press SHIFT F3 to bring up the V-Window

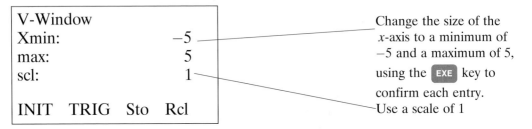

```
V-Window
Xmin:              −5
max:                5
scl:                1

INIT  TRIG  Sto  Rcl
```

Change the size of the x-axis to a minimum of −5 and a maximum of 5, using the EXE key to confirm each entry.
Use a scale of 1

Press the down arrow key to produce a similar window for y and change the y-axis from −5 to 5, using a scale of 1, again.

Exercise 18I   Graphical calculator

1 Draw four different lines parallel to $y = x + 1$.

2 Draw four different lines parallel to $y = 2x − 1$.

3 Draw four different non-parallel lines but all passing through the point (0, 2).

4 Draw four different lines with a steeper gradient than $y = x$ and all passing through the origin.

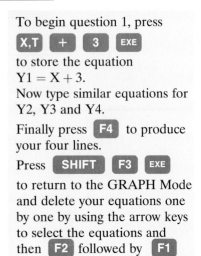

To begin question 1, press
X,T + 3 EXE
to store the equation
Y1 = X + 3.
Now type similar equations for Y2, Y3 and Y4.

Finally press F4 to produce your four lines.

Press SHIFT F3 EXE
to return to the GRAPH Mode and delete your equations one by one by using the arrow keys to select the equations and then F2 followed by F1

5 Draw four different lines with a shallower gradient than $y = x$.

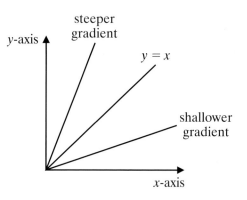

6 Shown below are two lines which are a reflection of each other in the line $x = 0$. Enter the two equations on your calculator and draw the two lines.

The line $x = 0$ is another name for the y-axis.

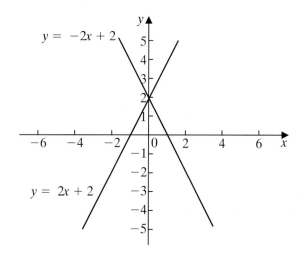

Draw two other lines which are reflections of each other in the line $x = 0$ and are:

(a) steeper than the two given lines and passing through the point $(0, 1)$

(b) shallower than the two given lines and passing through the point $(0, 1)$

(c) steeper than the two given lines and passing through the point $(0, -2)$

(d) shallower than the two given lines and passing through the point $(0, 2)$.

7 Below is the curve $y = x^2$. Enter the equation on your calculator and draw the curve.

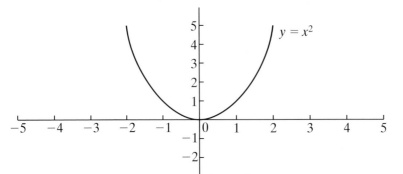

Draw a curve with equation $y = ax^2$ which is

(a) narrower than $y = x^2$

(b) wider than $y = x^2$.

a can be a whole number or fraction.

b is a whole number.

Draw a curve with equation $y = x^2 + b$ which

(c) passes through (0, 2)

(d) passes through (0, −3).

An alternative way to do this exercise is to use a computer software package like Omnigraph.

A third way would be to use a spreadsheet. You will have to create the points in a similar way to Chapter 12 by using the columns on your spreadsheet.

	A	B
1	x	y
2	−3	−3
3	−2	−1
4	−1	1
5	0	3
6	1	5
7	2	7
8	3	9

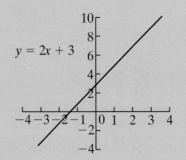

- −3 was entered in cell A2.
- = A2 + 1 was entered in cell A3.
- = 2*A2 + 3 was entered in cell B2.

18.10 Fractions

You can use the fraction key on your calculator to answer the type of questions you met in Unit 3.

Your fraction key may look like this: $a^b/_c$

Example 6

(a) Find $\frac{2}{3}$ of £39.81.

(b) Reduce $\frac{90}{135}$ to its lowest terms.

(c) Place the following fractions in order of size, starting with the smallest

$\frac{11}{13}, \frac{7}{9}, \frac{21}{26}, \frac{6}{7}, \frac{16}{19}$

(d) Change the mixed number $16\frac{12}{17}$ into an improper fraction.

(e) Change $\frac{423}{17}$ to a mixed number.

(f) Calculate $\frac{5}{11} + \frac{11}{13}$.

(a) Press:

Answer: £26.54

> Press the multiplication key for 'of'
> so $\frac{2}{3}$ of £39.81 is the same as $\frac{2}{3} \times$ £39.81

(b) Press:

[9] [0] [$a^b/_c$] [1] [3] [5] [=]

Answer: $\frac{2}{3}$

> The fraction button always displays the fraction in its simplest form.

(c) Calculate the decimal equivalent of each fraction to help order them.

Press:

$\frac{11}{13} = 0.846153846\ldots$

$\frac{7}{9} = 0.777777777\ldots$

$\frac{21}{26} = 0.807692307\ldots$

$\frac{6}{7} = 0.857142857\ldots$

$\frac{16}{19} = 0.842105263\ldots$

Answer: $\frac{7}{9}, \frac{21}{26}, \frac{16}{19}, \frac{11}{13}, \frac{6}{7}$

> To find the decimal equivalent you divide the numerator of the fraction by the denominator.

> There is more about ordering decimals on p. 79

(d) Press:

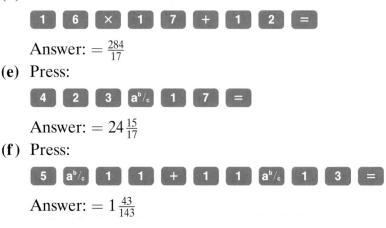

Answer: $= \frac{284}{17}$

(e) Press:

Answer: $= 24\frac{15}{17}$

(f) Press:

Answer: $= 1\frac{43}{143}$

Exercise 18J   Scientific calculator

1 Calculate:

(a) $\frac{3}{5}$ of £63.45   (b) $\frac{7}{9}$ of £167.76   (c) $\frac{11}{12}$ of $625.32

2 Reduce these fractions to their lowest terms.

(a) $\frac{140}{252}$ (b) $\frac{176}{192}$ (c) $\frac{264}{282}$

(d) $\frac{57}{76}$ (e) $\frac{315}{560}$ (f) $\frac{78}{234}$

3 Place these fractions in order of size starting with the smallest.

$\frac{27}{28}, \frac{35}{36}, \frac{16}{17}, \frac{12}{13}, \frac{55}{59}$

4 Change these mixed numbers to improper fractions.

(a) $13\frac{5}{9}$ (b) $23\frac{14}{17}$ (c) $9\frac{17}{19}$ (d) $45\frac{56}{57}$

5 Change these improper fractions to mixed numbers.

(a) $\frac{165}{132}$ (b) $\frac{203}{19}$ (c) $\frac{433}{212}$ (d) $\frac{1965}{18}$

6 Calculate:

(a) $\frac{3}{11} + \frac{15}{16}$ (b) $\frac{21}{43} - \frac{17}{45}$ (c) $\frac{7}{12} + \frac{13}{17} + \frac{9}{10}$ (d) $\frac{12}{13} - \frac{1}{17} + \frac{5}{9}$

(e) $\frac{4}{11} \div \frac{3}{7}$ (f) $\frac{5}{12} \times \frac{18}{35}$ (g) $\frac{4}{13} \times \frac{13}{14} \div \frac{3}{7}$ (h) $\frac{7}{11} + \frac{3}{5} \times \frac{4}{9}$

7 Calculate:

(a) $\frac{3}{5} \times 45$ (b) $12\frac{3}{5} + 2\frac{5}{9}$ (c) $13\frac{5}{7} \div 3\frac{3}{7}$ (d) $23\frac{1}{5} - 8\frac{7}{9}$

(e) $19 \div 2\frac{2}{3}$ (f) $13 - 5\frac{7}{11}$ (g) $\frac{2\frac{3}{5}}{\frac{4}{9}}$ (h) $\frac{\frac{5}{32}}{16}$

Exercise 18K   Scientific calculator

The 24 Puzzle

In the table opposite:

- Select any block of four numbers. Some possible groupings are highlighted.
- Using **all** four numbers and any of the mathematical signs $+$, $-$, $\times$, $\div$ create a total of 24.
- You may use brackets.
- Placing two digits together to make a number like 36 is not allowed.

1	2	3	4
5	6	7	8
9	1	2	3
4	5	6	7
8	9	1	2
3	4	5	6
7	8	9	1
2	3	4	5
6	7	8	9

Example 7

(a) Choose 1, 2, 3 and 4:

$$1 \times 2 \times 3 \times 4 = 24$$

(b) Choose 2, 3, 6 and 7:

$$(7 - 3) \times (8 - 2) = 24$$

18.11 Transformations and tessellations

Every time you start WinLogo, or clear the screen, the turtle position is reset to $(0, 0)$. You can change the position of the turtle by using the setpos command.

You clear the screen by typing in cs

Example 8

This example uses `square 1` and `rectangle 1` which you created on p. 305.

Remember:
Type in pu to lift the **pen up** and pd to put the **pen down**

(a) Draw square1 and then translate it 50 units to the right.

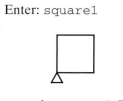

Enter: square1

... to draw square1. The cursor ends up at the point $(0, 0)$

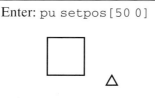

Enter: pu setpos [50 0]

... to move the cursor to the point $(50, 0)$

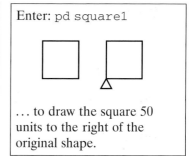

Enter: pd square1

... to draw the square 50 units to the right of the original shape.

(b) Draw `rectangle1` and translate it 40 units to the **left** and 60 units **up**.

Type and enter:

`cs rectangle1 pu setpos [-40 60] pd rectangle1`

                                        −40 moves 40 units to the left
                                          60 moves 60 units up

Exercise 18L   WinLogo

1 Create the following translations from [0, 0]

  (a) move `square1` 80 units right

  (b) move `rectangle2` 40 units right and 50 units up

  (c) move `rectangle1` 60 units right and 40 units down

  (d) move `flag1` 70 units left and 40 units up

  (e) move `flag2` 90 units left and 30 units down

Remember to clear the screen between each translation.

Example 9 – Reflections

Draw `rectangle2` and reflect it in the line of symmetry shown.

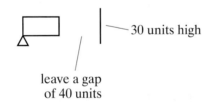

30 units high

leave a gap
of 40 units

Type and enter:

`cs rectangle2 pu setpos [80 0] pd fd 30 pu`
`setpos [120 0] pd rectangle2`

Exercise 18M   WinLogo

1 Draw the following shapes and lines of symmetry on screen and then their image after a reflection in the given line of symmetry. Use the shapes that you created earlier.

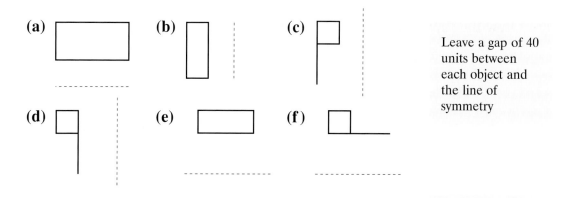

Leave a gap of 40 units between each object and the line of symmetry

Click:
Bitmap and Print to obtain a copy of your lines of symmetry

2 Draw, in different positions in the same WinLogo window, `rectangle1`, `rectangle2` and `square1`. Add all lines of symmetry to each shape.

Example 10 – Rotations

Rotate `rectangle1` 90° anticlockwise using the turtle position [0 0] as the centre of rotation.

Type and enter:

```
rectangle1 rt 90 rectangle1
```

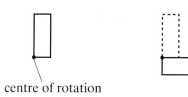

centre of rotation

Exercise 18N   WinLogo

1 Draw the following shapes and their image following the given rotation:

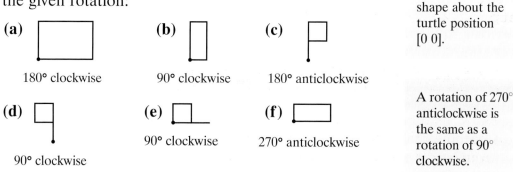

Rotate each shape about the turtle position [0 0].

A rotation of 270° anticlockwise is the same as a rotation of 90° clockwise.

2 Draw the following tessellations on screen

(a)

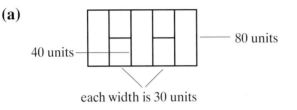

40 units

80 units

each width is 30 units

(b)

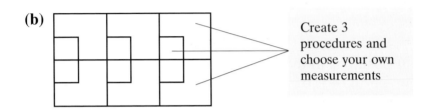

Create 3 procedures and choose your own measurements

Example 11 – Enlargements

Create a procedure called growsquare:

```
to growsquare
repeat 4 [fd :x rt 90]
end
```

Don't forget the colon

Typing in growsquare at the commander will draw a square of side x. You can use this routine to draw enlargements.

Type in:

```
make "x 20 growsquare
```

to draw a square of side 20.

Type in:

```
make "x 40 growsquare
```

to draw a square of side 40 – an enlargement of scale factor 2.

You can use letters to represent numbers in WinLogo:
`make "x 20`
means let x equal 20.

Exercise 18O   WinLogo

1 Continue changing the value of x to produce a sequence of enlarged squares with side 60, 80, 100 and 120 units.

2 Type and enter:

cs make "x 20 repeat 6 [growsquare make "x :x+20]

and then:

make "x 0 repeat 7 [growsquare make "x :x−20]

Describe the connection between the squares drawn.

3 Write a procedure to produce a rectangle with length x and width y units.
Starting with x = 20 and y = 40 units, enlarge the rectangle by a scale factor of 3.

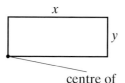

x

y

centre of
enlargement, (0 0)

4 Enlarge flag1 (page 305) by a scale factor of 2 from a centre of enlargement at the base of the flag pole.

Index